Our Wildlife Heritage

100 years of Wildlife Management

The sea otter "... a furred, webfooted aquatic mammal" that hastened the rush to explore coastal British Columbia.

Our Wildlife Heritage

100 years of
Wildlife Management

Published by
The Centennial Wildlife Society
of British Columbia
1987

Publication of this book was made possible by financial assistance from:
    The Ministry of Environment and Parks
    The B.C. Lottery Fund

COVER PHOTO: *Steller's Jay*, courtesy Tim Zurowski.
Illustrations by Jack Grundle, courtesy Ministry
of Environment and Parks.

Designed and Printed in Canada by
MORRISS PRINTING COMPANY LTD.
Victoria, British Columbia

Contents

Photos follow page 96.

Preface

One hundred years ago, in 1887, the Government of Canada recognized the value of wildlife by setting aside for protection a water body in Saskatchewan. It was probably the first such designation in North America. This year it is being celebrated across Canada by wildlife agencies and friends.

In this province the Centennial Wildlife Society of British Columbia was established to arrange appropriate events and projects to mark the important anniversary. This book is one such project.

The value of wildlife reflects different perceptions. A finch on a feeder, a skein of north-flying geese, a bugling elk, a frog in the grubby hands of a school boy, all have an intrinsic value in that moment in time that defies economic analysis or, to use a stylish word, prioritization. It was with that thought in mind that the committee chose to have this book written by a dozen different people, each reflecting his or her own values and perceptions.

The problems inherent is getting a dozen people to write to a deadline and to more or less follow the guidelines of an editor were overcome by their enthusiasm and willingness to set aside private schedules and commitments. They researched and wrote the following chapters in a short time and have put together, for the first time, the story of wildlife management in British Columbia during the past 100 years. They get the lion's share of credit for this book.

But authors are not the only people responsible for producing a book. Special thanks goes to Lynda Adams and Lynne Foxall for typing and retyping the manuscript. Lee Straight took on the task of copy editing the hundreds of pages to typewritten manuscript. Dick Morriss of Morriss Printing and his publishing house staff deserve thanks for their guidance and patience. The Centennial Society itself, of course, gets special credit for sponsoring the project.

In particular, appreciation is due W. Winston "Bill" Mair, chairman of the Society, for his optimism that it could be done and his thoughtful and knowledgeable comments; and to Edwin H. Vernon, treasurer of the Society, for looking after the financing. J. H. C. Walker, director of the Wildlife Branch, was always supportive. Nancy James very capably looked after the distribution of the pre-publication orders.

The views and interpretations expressed are those of the individual authors. They may not be shared by other authors, the editor, or the Centennial Society. No attempt was made to tailor them to any specific philosophy except that wildlife is important to all of us.

The writing styles are peculiar to each author; no attempt was made to homogenize them other than a brief introduction to each chapter by the editor. The diversity of views and styles reflects, in a small way, the wealth of wildlife diversity that enriches the lives of so many British Columbians.

Errors, of course, remain the responsibility of the editor who is grateful for the help and support of all of the above.

Allan Murray, *editor*
Victoria, October, 1987

"*The economy of nature and the ecology of man are inseparable and attempts to separate them are more than misleading, they are dangerous. Man's destiny is tied to nature's destiny and the arrogance of the engineering mind does not change this. Man may be a very peculiar animal, but he is still a part of the system of nature.*"

Marston Bates
The Forest and The Sea

Introduction

ALLAN MURRAY

The first humans to enter British Columbia may well have been hunters from the top of the world hot on the trail of mammoths. Mammoths represented survival in a fierce and unrelenting environment. Archeological evidence supports this theory and while it is not without its skeptics one thing is clear, wildlife and people have lived together in this part of the Pacific northwest for centuries, perhaps for millennia. It is inconceivable to picture British Columbia without wildlife.

Not much changed in that relationship for hundreds of years. Men did not have the capacity to seriously damage wildlife populations. Natural forces prevailed; it is reasonable to assume that periods of scarcity followed periods of plenty. Starvation, or at least lean times, may well have been a visitor to early life in British Columbia. Times of feast were probably common, as well. There is little evidence on which to draw an accurate portrait of those years.

But in the last century great changes have taken place and much of what happened is a matter of record. To some considerable degree the story of wildlife management is the story of provincial development. Home use, trade, regulation, law enforcement, commerce; each stage in the growth of the province is reflected in wildlife management. The chapters following illustrate the use and importance of wildlife in a growing economy that was, and is, based on natural resource exploitation.

Just as wildlife sustained white settlers 100 years or so ago, wildlife and fish sustained the first inhabitants of British Columbia many centuries earlier. They not only provided food and clothing, they also provided cultural resources that are still evident in totems, masks, and other carvings.

But all this was to change when the Spanish navigator Juan Perez met a group of Haidas on the northwest point of Langara Island in 1774. The crew of the *Santiago* traded some odds and ends from their ship for some sea otter furs and some hand-made articles such as carved plates, spoons and hats. The exchange was peaceable. The Indians threw feathers on the water around the ship to indicate their peaceful intentions. But they were not so incautious as to board the ship, presumably the first they had seen.

The sea-based fur trade began in earnest in 1785 when James Hanna arrived in Nootka to begin trading in furs. His vessel was appropriately named the *Sea Otter*. He found he was dealing, not with gullible and naïve savages, but with a people who knew what they wanted in trade and who, to a considerable extent, controlled the trade, at least to the extent that they were able to preserve much of their culture in those early years. It was a mutually beneficial trading relationship. In the Pacific northwest, at least, furs for beads is more myth than reality.

The land-based fur trade was also equally beneficial to both parties, unlike the reported inequalities that marked the fur trade east of the Rockies.

The early traders and settlements quickly, through necessity, learned the value of wildlife for sustenance. They learned from the Indians. Miners, ranchers, railroad contractors, and virtually everyone else who set foot in British Columbia in those early days lived, in whole or in part, on wildlife. British Columbia would have been discovered, developed, and settled even if there had been no wildlife here. But clearly the abundance of wildlife, sea mammals and terrestrial, hastened the pace of settlement.

Wildlife and the pursuit of it helped shape the physical and social environment of this province. To the extent that our environment shapes us as a people, we are indebted to wildlife for its contribution.

But with settlement came pressure on the resource. Pressure requires response. Since 1616, when the first wildlife protective legislation was passed in North America, people have responded to pressure by making rules. The first laws were proclamations passed by the Government of Bermuda for the protection of cahows and the green turtle. Robins came under the protection of the government of Massachusetts in 1818. In 1859 a law was passed in British Columbia protecting wildlife. Since then an endless parade of legislation has been trotted forth in the continuing struggle to balance protection with use.

Once a law is established it seems to be human nature to challenge it. Law breakers follow law makers as surely as night follows day. Catching them is a challenging and costly process. Not catching them is even more costly to the resource.

The man with the gun has come to be regarded, in some circles, as the villain in the conservation wars. If the hunter is a villain, mankind has been villainous since the dawn of time. We have hunted and killed animals since we first picked up a stone and threw it. The animals have survived and so have we. Some hunters were greedy, others were venal, some have been just plain ignorant. But far and away most have been good people following a time-honoured tradition. The hunter today may well be the most important supporter of strong

12

wildlife populations. His money has certainly been a major contributor to wildlife management.

Indeed, much of the support for scientific management has come from organized hunters who could see, or perhaps just feel, that strong emotions were not enough to manage wildlife. Many, some would say most, of the wildlife scientific community came from the ranks of people who grew up with hunting and the outdoors. But wherever they came from, scientists have brought a whole new dimension to wildlife management. Increasing pressure on the land requires increased sophistication, leavened with a respect and love for the creatures themselves.

But if the science of the biologist has lead to better management, and indeed it has, the "science" of the big game guide has led to more successful hunts. The people who know where to go, what to do, and when to do it have always been in demand. The Indians first filled that role when they helped Alexander Mackenzie find his way across the mountains to the Pacific. Later, it was men who lived on the edge of settlement and sometimes even on the edge of society who took the greenhorn and led him to the big buck. And in the process, acquainted him with some of the wonders of the land and the animals that lived there.

Closely akin were the predator hunters who responded to society's clamour that predators be destroyed. More than 350 years ago the Massachusetts authorities put a one penny bounty on wolves. Legislators ever since have been trying to placate the folks who see predators as competition for what they want. The predator hunters were often colourful men, with real skill, who could think like their quarry. Some never regretted their devotion to predator killing. Others look back with chagrin at what they see now as misguided endeavour.

Misguided endeavour was not peculiar to the men who chased predators. Society itself was often misguided and, in turn, the legislators reacted with foolishness. But there were those whose instincts were usually good and whose advice, if not always well considered, was at least well intentioned. People of like mind often band together to achieve a common goal. The goal could be as lofty as getting the Magna Carta signed by a reluctant king or as mundane as getting a reluctant minister to change bag limit for mallards. Indeed, kings and carpenters have joined forces with captains and shoe clerks to protect the wildlife they hold dear. Their efforts have been valiant and valuable.

Not all citizen associations were bound by a liking for the gun. Many were naturalists whose delight was in seeing not shooting wildlife. While the hunting fraternity willingly paid licence fees to hunt, and indeed, implored governments to increase the fees so more

13

money would be available to wildlife managers, the naturalists contributed through the production of scholarly papers ranging from geology and anthropology to native fauna and entomology.

In more recent times the animal rights movement has attracted public attention and adherents. More militant, more aggressive, more unorthodox than the traditional wildlife advocate groups, the animal rights associations have presented a quite different philosophical argument about why animals should be left alone. They have also used quite different tactics to get the attention of the legislators and the public. The prize is what counts, they argue, and the prize for them is an untrammelled and free wildlife.

But whether one hunts animals, or looks at them, or advocates, by whatever method, their well being, the bottom line is surely habitat. Someone once said that "Greed shows up more clearly on a landscape that on a man's face, and so does kindness." How well or poorly we treat the landscape — the habitat of our wildlife heritage — indicates the degree of kindness that drives our endeavours on the land. Society's face will surely show our greed or kindness.

"Ever since Adam and Eve, ejected from Eden, first donned the skins of wild beasts, fur has been a spectacular talisman. In the delicate interplay between sensibility and fashion, practicality and luxury, the wearing of furs has retained a savage symbolic undercurrent of potency, success and brute strength — bestowing on its wearer an aura of wild beauty, magic powers and social cachet."

Peter C. Newman
Company of Adventurers

The sea otter is described as a "furred, webfooted aquatic mammal . . . that feeds exclusively on fish." It can, with equal accuracy, be described as the spur to exploration of the Pacific northwest. British Columbia, as much as any region in Canada, owes its early development to the lust for furs to satisfy the fashions of Europe and the lust for money to satisfy the hearts, and the pocket books, of the traders.

It also satisfied the needs of the Indians who entered the trade, according to some scholars, not as ignorant or naïve savages, but as people well versed in matters of trade.

But it obviously couldn't last — fur supplies diminished, adventurers followed the traders, gold seekers pushed into the wilderness, the first signs of pressure on the habitat. Animal populations fluctuated, and, despite what people may say, the Hudson's Bay Company practiced a rude form of wildlife management in an effort to sustain populations.

In more recent times, far greater pressure has been put on the industry by the anti-trapping groups. The industry's belated response of more humane trapping methods may be too little too late to satisfy the largely urban conservationists who want everyone to leave nature, especially fur bearers, alone.

Whatever its future, its past should not be ignored or denigrated. Trapping played a useful role in the development of Canada, indeed in the determination of national boundaries. Indian and non-Indian trappers were not villains or sadists: they were hardy people making a living in a harsh environment providing a product that the rest of society wanted and was willing to pay for.

Today they are fewer in number, but the demand remains. The modern British Columbia trapper goes about his business with a newer and more humane technology, but with the same sense of symbiosis with the animals themselves.

CHAPTER 1

The Fur Trade — B.C.'s First Industry

James Hatter

Had it not been for the fur trade, the Stars and Stripes would now wave over British Columbia. If the British Hudson's Bay Company in 1858 had not been established on the Pacific frontier, the tens of thousands of American gold-seekers could and would have successfully demanded American control of this territory. It is only because Chief Factor James Douglas of the Hudson's Bay Company immediately imposed British authority on the hordes of American miners on their way to the Fraser River goldfields, which action led to the consequent proclamation of the colony of British Columbia, that this territory is now a part of Canada. Moreover, the boundaries of Canada are essentially a result of the expansion of the fur trade across this country.

The first European to trade with the Indians for furs in Canada (for the sake of convenience, the territories encompassing what is now Vancouver Island, British Columbia and Canada will be referred to by these names) was Jacques Cartier in 1534. Two and one-half centuries later, in 1778, Captain James Cook landed at Nootka on the west coast of Vancouver Island. Both of those famous explorers were searching for a waterway or passage between the Atlantic and Pacific Oceans. Cartier knew that furs would be valuable cargo to take back to Europe, but Cook's men acquired sea otter pelts and garments from the Nootka Indians, not as items of commerce, but for warm clothing to wear during their sea voyage northward in search of a route to the Atlantic.

On the return voyage, Captain Cook was killed by Hawaiians. His company and crew stopped at Macao (near Canton) on their return journey. While there, the members of the crew sold the sea otter clothes they had bartered for at Nootka for an incredible profit. A few cents' worth of iron goods brought the equivalent of 12 golden guineas of furs.

In Atlantic Canada, the beaver dominated the fur trade because its fur was required for the manufacture of felt hats. But after the publications of Cook's voyage, the sea otter became the most prized of all furs. Henceforth, a vigorous, uncontrolled trade developed. European traders, led by Englishman James Hanna in 1785, and American traders from Boston, quickly entered the lucrative business as there was a ready market for sea otter pelts in China. By the end of the eighteenth century, almost all European traders were restricted to the Atlantic because of the Napoleonic Wars and the consequent blockades. The Pacific coast was then left to the unfettered and aggressive American traders and, in Alaska, to the Russian-American Company. The competition intensified and, from 1796 to 1803, between 10,000 and 15,000 sea otters were killed annually. No figures are available for the total number of pelts obtained along the British Columbia and Alaska coast by British or American traders during the busy thirty-year period from 1785 to 1814. But it has been estimated that American traders alone collected 48,000 sea otter skins in the four peak years from 1799 to 1802.

According to Georgiana Ball, a British Columbia historian, it is possible that coastal Indians participated in the extirpation of the sea otter because the animal was not required for their survival. The otter pelt was a luxury, not a necessity. Newly-acquired tastes, acquisitiveness, and potlatch gift requirements, however, created a demand, not only for iron, but also for non-metallic goods such as cloth, rice, bread, molasses, rum, ermine skins, and ornaments. To pay for these items, the Indians killed thousands upon thousands of sea otters because their pelts brought the most trade goods.

During the evolution of Vancouver Island and British Columbia from separate colonies to become one province of Canada in 1871, the sea otter trade continued, but the numbers drastically declined.

The following table shows the average number of sea otter skins per year taken by Canadian vessels from waters off British Columbia, Alaska and probably, Siberia during the closing years of the sea otter trade. (The first year for which statistics are available is 1879.)

Years	Annual Average # Skins	Average Price
1879-81	98	$ 40.00
1882-83, 1885-86	97	53.00
1887-1890	98	84.00
1892-96	16	120.00
1897-98, 1900-01	28	325.00
1902, 1904, 1906	10	437.00
1907, 1911	21	552.00

The decline after 1891 in the harvest from the Bering Sea is attributed to temporary agreements in 1891, 1892 and 1893 which prohibited sealing (as well as otter hunting) in these northern waters. The ten-fold increase in value of the pelts is a further indicator of greatly reduced availability.

As a result of the International Fur Seal Convention of 1911, which also protected sea otters, there were subsequent otter recoveries along the Aleutian Archipelago and off California, but it was too late for those of British Columbia. The last recorded sea otter was seen in provincial waters in 1929. In 1982, the estimated total American population was 1,800 in California and 121,000 in Alaskan waters.

Once extinct on the British Columbia coast, the sea otter is now making a recovery. Eighty-nine animals were transplanted from Alaska to the west coast of Vancouver Island between 1969 and 1972. By May, 1984, the population had increased to 345 animals. This successful introduction is a happy ending to the sad story of sea otter extermination on this coast. The extinction of this species is a black mark in the history of the fur trade in British Columbia.

The northern fur seal, unlike the sea otter, is migratory, but it has had a history of uncontrolled competitive exploitation similar to that of the sea otter. It breeds on both the Russian and American coasts of the Bering Sea and migrates southwards through offshore waters as far as the coasts of California and Japan.

There were three types of sealing operation carried out by British Columbians. Off the coast of the province, the local Indians hunted from canoes along the shallow banks where the seals congregated to feed on fish. In 1876, the natives of Barclay Sound and those to the north procured about 2,600 fur seal pelts, according to Hudson's Bay Company records.

A second type of oceanic sealing was carried on from special sealing schooners which left Victoria city's harbour each spring for the undersea banks or shoals, ten to thirty miles offshore where the seals were known to feed during migrations in April, May and June. Unfortunately, the seals were mostly pregnant females, stopping to feed and rest en route north to the Pribilof Islands to give birth to their young. The hunting method employed by schooner sealers, according to one account, involved launching Indian canoes, each with two men, who made a cautious approach toward the sleeping seals; they then speared the seals to avoid the disturbance of shooting. The sealers clubbed any wounded seal that attacked their canoes. Aboard the schooner, the sealers attached weights to the skinned carcasses and discarded them overboard at a distance from the banks in order to avoid disturbing the remainder of the herd. The fact that so many female seals were killed in the oceanic sealing hastened their decline.

The third type of sealing involved the lengthy trip to the Bering Sea where seals were captured both offshore and on the breeding grounds. Victoria was the base for the sealing schooners and the port of departure for about 20 of them, some of which engaged in local open sea sealing while others made the long trip to the northern breeding grounds in the Bering Sea.

A Department of Fisheries and Marine report for 1894 records the fur seal catch by the British Columbia sealing fleet out of Victoria as follows:

British Columbia coast	11,703
Japanese coast	48,993
Copper Island (Commanderofski Is.)	7,437
Bering Sea	26,341
	94,474

Value @ $10 per pelt = $944,740.00.

These were the halcyon days of sealing. The catches dropped significantly during the following decade.

By 1910, the breeding population on the Pribilof Islands had been reduced to about 200,000 animals, or an estimated 5 per cent of the probable original numbers. An international fur seal convention in 1911, between the United States, Russia, Japan and Great Britain (acting for Canada), outlawed all oceanic sealing except by aborigines using original native methods.

The seal population rebounded after the prohibition of pelagic sealing, with its heavy toll of females. Seals were taken on land and selectively harvested to maintain the most productive level, which was about 1,500,000 for the Pribilofs. Canada received a share of the land harvest from the Pribilof Islands, even though fur seals have only a temporary residence in British Columbia waters. In recent years the population has declined to less than 800,000 due apparently to net entanglement. The annual harvest has stopped.

About the time the fierce competition between the British and Americans for the sea otter trade ended, the land traders arrived in British Columbia. Bitter, and sometimes bloody, rivalry between the traders of the Northwest Company out of Montreal and the Hudson's Bay Company, headquartered in London, was devastating the beaver population of the Canadian Shield and the prairies. The westward expansion of trade opened up the Athabasca and Peace River country, not only to traders, but also to outside trappers. Because the Plains Indians were not interested in trapping as long as they could kill bison in sufficient numbers to provide themselves with food, shelter and clothing, the traders brought Iroquois and Ojibway hunters from the east to scour the prairies, chiefly for beaver. The traders moved the alien Indian trappers, along with their steel traps, into the best beaver country in British Columbia, the upper Peace River watershed, which is the home of the Sekanni and Beaver Indians.

The local Indians did not approve of this invasion of their tribal hunting grounds — land which had been passed down from family to family for generations. The animals they used for food and clothing and the land on which they fished and hunted were considered the property of families or clans, or both, who traditionally fished and hunted there. These traditions were the subject of great pride. Because of this recognized ownership, the resident Indians looked after the animal resources and did not deplete the game and fish upon which their lives depended.

The Iroquois depleted the beaver because they had no vested interest in the country. Some of them even moved into Carrier country in the Fraser Lake region, and the Carriers threatened to kill the intruders. When their warnings were not heeded, the Carriers killed an Iroquois trapper and his wife and two children.

The competition for the depleted fur resources in the Athabasca and Peace regions brought about further westward movement across the Rockies by the Northwest Company shortly after the XY Company joined it in 1804. The new company chose Simon Fraser to open up the area across the mountains to the west. By 1808, Fraser and his second-in-command, John Stuart, had established the trading posts Rocky Mountain House Portage, Fort McLeod, Fort St. James, Fort George and Fort Fraser, and explored the Fraser River to its estuary. Fraser named the region served by the four last posts, New Caledonia.

Westward movement was in progress at the same time in the southern regions of the province. David Thompson, a former employee of the Hudson's Bay Company and now one of the Northwest Company's trader-explorers, left the Saskatchewan River in 1807 and crossed the Rockies by way of Howse Pass, explored the Kootenay country and established Kootenay House near Lake Windermere. In 1811, he discovered Athabasca Pass (Yellowhead Pass) and proceeded to the Columbia which he descended to its mouth. There he found an American fur trading post, Fort Astoria, owned by John Jacob Astor's Pacific Fur Company. Thompson built four trading posts in the Columbia region for the Northwest Company and, in 1812, the company bought out Astor's Pacific Fur Company's assets on the lower Columbia in what is now Oregon. The Northwest Company thus had control of the inland fur trade all the way from the Spanish possessions in what is now California in the south to Russian Alaska in the north.

While the Northwest Company was expanding to the west and south in the Pacific Northwest, the Hudson's Bay Company was moving into the Peace River country and giving the former company severe competition. The Northwesters were incurring huge expenses due to their expansion and the only way to meet these high costs was to scour the country of furs both east and west of the Rockies. There could be no consideration for conservation. This was competition at its worst and it was not only highly damaging to the fur populations but also financially ruinous for both companies. To recover from their losses, the two companies amalgamated in 1821 under the name of the Hudson's Bay Company. The new company received monopoly rights from the British government to trade with the Indians west of the Rockies for a period of twenty-one years.

In the areas depleted by the competition of the rival companies, conservation practices were now possible. However, there was still competition in the south from American land traders, in the north from the Russians and, on the coast, from the American sea traders. In 1818, the United States and Great Britain agreed to a ten-year joint use of land west of the Rockies. The new Hudson's Bay Company, with the combined expertise and resources in manpower and trading posts, set about to protect its interests in New Caledonia from American trappers on the move westward. This was accomplished by establishing Fort Vancouver on the lower Columbia and from there sending large hunting and trapping expeditions to trap out the country south and east of the Columbia. A "fur desert" was created to act as a buffer zone to the incursion of American trappers and traders until Oregon became American territory in 1846.

Although the Hudson's Bay Company had a fur trade monopoly, there was no assurance that it would receive all the Indian trade from New Caledonia and further north. Furs were often passed by the Indians in trade from the interior to the coast where they were traded to American and Russian maritime traders. The Hudson's Bay Company decided to meet the challenge by putting five trading vessels on the coast of British Columbia between 1827 and 1836. By the mid-1830's, it was winning the sea trade battle with the Americans.

The Russian American Company, headquartered in Sitka, Alaska, depended upon the American sea traders bringing agricultural food-stuffs from New England because they could not produce them in Alaska. The round trip from Boston was becoming increasingly costly to the traders chiefly because of the depletion of the sea otter. In order to make a profit, it was necessary for the ships to carry outward cargo, hence the agreement with the Russians at Sitka to bring out food and other supplies. By the mid-1830's, the Hudson's Bay Company had extensive farms in the Columbia district. It produced a surplus, enough to satisfy the Russian requirements.

In a brilliant business manoeuvre, Governor George Simpson of the Hudson's Bay Company negotiated with the Russian American Company Governor, Baron Wrangell, to substitute the American food cargoes with produce from company farms. In 1839, the two men signed an agreement in Hamburg, Germany, by which the Russians rented the fur trading rights on the Alaska Panhandle to the British company in return for an annual rent which included farm produce. By the stroke of the pen, Simpson eliminated American competition on the coast by 1840 and, at the same time, allowed the company to stop the flow of furs from northern British Columbia to the Russian company.

For the most part, wildlife conservation practices are generally a product of the twentieth century. It is somewhat of a surprise, therefore, to realize that conservation measures were implemented by the Hudson's Bay Company in the heavily overtrapped regions east of the Rockies.

The beaver conservation initiatives east of the mountains were varied and many. They included closing or moving certain posts, offering higher prices for furs such as marten and muskrat, discouraging summer beaver trapping for food by providing summer employment for Indians and by selling fishing tackle cheaply. George Simpson banned the sale of leghold traps in all areas except frontier posts near the American border on the prairies and similar places where there was continual competition. Simpson considered steel traps a scourge because, unlike the pre-1790 Indian methods of using dogs and snares or spears, the steel traps resulted in non-selective killing. Simpson and his Council instituted a major conservation measure in 1826 which entailed beaver pelt quotas in fourteen depleted districts. Dunvegan (on the Peace River in present-day Alberta) was the only post taking furs from British Columbia to be included in the quota system. The quota was strictly enforced. Some of the company traders did not go along with the orders and, in 1841, a council regulation stipulated that there would be early retirement for traders who did not adhere strictly to the stated quotas.

Other than banning the use of steel traps and placing a quota on Peace River furs, George Simpson and his Council apparently considered protection of the Indian ownership traditions to be a sufficient conservation measure. The fact that only one post receiving British Columbia furs was assigned a beaver quota is a good indication that, for the most part, beaver populations in New Caledonia were still at a tolerable level. There was, however, a marked decline in the number of beaver pelts shipped from the interior of British Columbia in the 1840's, but the number rebounded in the 1850's. It appears, therefore, that responsible Indian hunters nursed their beaver stocks back to carrying capacity.

Shortly after 1821, the Hudson's Bay Company moved to the east all the Iroquois and other itinerant hunters. Consequently, the natives did not have to worry about poachers. They had monopoly control of their stocks and the control was protected by the Hudson's Bay Company. In this manner, the monopolistic Hudson's Bay Company, along with the Indians, managed its far-flung resources in a responsible way. The well-known Canadian historian, Harold A. Innis, in *The Fur Trade in Canada, An Introduction to Canadian Economic History*, concluded that "the existing evidence points to the effectiveness of monopoly control." It assures a steady supply of a wide range of furs in the face of natural fluctuations of furbearers and the market and, at the same time, controls fur production to prevent a flooded market.

The new colony of British Columbia was founded in 1858, at a time when monopolies were "contrary to the spirit of the time." The Hudson's Bay Company lost its exclusive Indian trade licence in British Columbia, and the colony was open to free enterprise entrepreneurs eager to exploit the natural resources. Centuries of monopoly control by Indian families and 37 years of a monopoly trading control by a company gave way in the last half of the nineteenth century to ineffectual control by uncertain public authority. The failure to regulate trapping until the end of the century may be attributed to the fact that furbearers were not considered game by sportsmen. Moreover, the early game laws applied only to organized districts in British Columbia. The law makers did not foresee the ill-effects of competition from free traders on populations of furbearing animals.

The value of furs and hides exported in 1868 has been estimated at $210,000 and in 1869, at a quarter of a million dollars. In 1871, the value of fur and hide exports declared at Customs was $246,387. From this time the export value of land fur remained fairly constant for the following three decades, even though fur prices decreased to very low levels. The fact that the export value of fur remained more or less constant indicates a significant increase in the number of skins sold. The free traders who sold their furs in Victoria rivalled and often exceeded the Hudson's Bay Company in the total value of land furs exported annually. This encouraged others to enter the unregulated industry.

Some traders built their own posts in competition with the Hudson's Bay Company and invested heavily in desired trade goods. These traders had a competitive advantage in that the Hudson's Bay Company's post managers were inhibited in their fur buying by a strict tariff imposed by the Committee in London. Because they received higher prices in Victoria from the fur merchants compared to the Hudson's Bay Company's London prices, the free traders could afford to buy some furs at a loss in order to obtain most or all of an Indian trapper's catch, which would include the select skins. The highly competitive trading among the free traders and between them and the Hudson's Bay Company in the latter part of the nineteenth century resulted in a substantial reduction in furbearing animals, particularly of beaver. The depletion was most severe in the more heavily populated areas, as a result of competition from white trappers.

It was not until 1896 that the government passed laws to protect unprime beaver, marten and river otters between April 1 and November 1. Beaver continued to decline and, in 1905, a six-year closed

24

season was put into effect. This appears to have been an over-reaction to the beaver decline. The Hudson's Bay Company argued that the ban was unwarranted in northern British Columbia and that the Indian trappers were not over-trapping. They also argued that, if the Order in Council superseded tribal laws and customs, indiscriminate slaughter of beaver would result and, because of the lack of enforcement officers, pelts would be smuggled out and sold in other provinces. The Company's arguments were effective and the trapping ban was lifted for Indians north of a line running east and west through the confluence of the Blackwater River and the Fraser. The exemption lasted only two years because it was impossible to enforce. Beaver populations expanded rapidly and, in 1910, A. Bryan Williams, the first provincial Game Warden, did not recommend an extension. But when the season opened on November 1, 1911, the trapping pressure was so heavy that a new order-in-council in 1912 declared another closed season, effective until November 15, 1913. This time, the Indians of the Stikine, Liard and Peace river watersheds were exempted from the closure.

In 1913, a $10 trapper's licence for whites only was introduced which allowed the holder to hunt and trap. In addition, all fur traders were required to submit an annual return to the Provincial Game Warden, stating number and species of pelts purchased. It was not until 1914 that fox, fisher, mink, muskrat, raccoon and weasel were added to the list of furbearers seasonally protected by the Game Act. Trapping restrictions were virtually impossible to enforce, however, over much of the province. To the credit of the Game Conservation Board of the day, it found a solution that left a good part of the responsibility of furbearer conservation up to the individual trapper. It introduced the registered trapline system in British Columbia, the first jurisdiction in North America to do so. This return to a form of monopoly control was innovated in 1925 and put into effect during the ensuing ten years.

The Crown lands of the province are divided up into traplines to which the individual registered trapper has exclusive trapping rights. In effect, the trapper has a mini-monopoly which allows him to manage his animal population for sustained yield. To understand the importance of this, we only have to recall what happened to the sea otter, the fur seal and the beaver under the competitive free-for-all during the darker period of our fur trade history.

When we look back on the early history of British Columbia and read about the amazing exploits of such famous men as Alexander Mackenzie, Simon Fraser and David Thompson, we realize that the driving force behind their exploration was primarily the quest for furs. The beaver, the marten and the many other furbearing animals of our province have played an important role in shaping our history.

In present-day British Columbia, the annual production of fur-bearing animals exceeds that of the past century. While ranking only sixth among the Canadian provinces in fur production, the value of British Columbia's fur resources to the trapper varies between 3.5 and 5 million dollars annually.

The role of the early trading companies in the harvest of fur has been taken over by provincial governments. The dominant Hudson's Bay Company, after more than three centuries, is no longer in the fur business. The Indian trapper is no longer the only fur harvester, and non-Indian trappers about equal the Indian trappers in numbers.

European culture and lifestyle have largely over-run the protective stewardship of the early native hunters, whose lives depended on beaver and other animals. No longer does the Indian trap mostly for food and clothing, as he did before he adopted the culture of the non-Indian. In many instances, he is having to learn how to trap from the invader because the latter has so destroyed the aboriginal lifestyle that native tradition and practices are no longer handed down from generation to generation. The production of fur from Indian traplines in British Columbia is below that of non-Indian trappers in many areas.

Most of the fur harvest is now sold through fur auction houses in Toronto and Vancouver. The role of the independent fur trader in buying and trading in furs has largely disappeared. There are still fur buyers who deal directly with trappers, but the advantage of auction selling has made it much less profitable to sell directly to a fur buyer.

Very few British Columbia trappers depend upon trapping for their total income, although the fur harvest is still economically important, especially in the north. Today, many people, including doctors, teachers and other professional people, are part-time trappers. The economic benefits of the trapline are often secondary to the pleasure of days in the wilderness away from the hustle and clatter of urban living. Often criticized for killing animals, the trapper is seldom recognized for his close association with nature and his unrecorded observations of natural wilderness, which he is among the first to defend against destruction.

In addition to registered traplines, there are private property traplines on which the landowner may grant trapping privileges to persons licenced to trap. This is usually carried on after work, on days off, or on weekends. Sometimes it is called recreational trapping but even casual trappers will probably agree that recreation is not accurately descriptive because, even close to home, sub-zero weather and deep snow can be uncomfortable, tiring and demanding of endurance and survival ability, conditions that are not usually associated with recreational pursuits. Technology, however, has made life easier for the trapper with the replacement of snowshoes, dog-teams and canoes by airplane, four-wheel drive vehicles, all-terrain vehicles and snowmobiles.

Markedly different from historic times are the modern methods used to catch furbearers. British Columbia has been in the forefront of humane trapping methods. The much-publicized leghold trap is no longer legal to use for such species as marten, weasels, fisher, raccoon, wolverine and squirrels. It can be used only for water animals such as beaver, otter, muskrats and mink, where the trap is used in drowning situations. Aquatic furbearers have a system of valves that prevent water entering the lungs if they are drowned. Wolves, coyotes, foxes, lynx and bobcat cannot be caught in foothold traps unless the traps have offset jaws or rubber pads. New humane traps that kill instantly or very quickly are required in British Columbia for most upland species such as marten, fisher and raccoon. Continuing humane trap research is very much a feature of modern trapping. The Conibear trap, invented by Frank Conibear of Victoria, is the first of the more humane traps. It is used extensively today. One of the early and well-known white trappers, Eric Collier of Riske Creek near Williams Lake, assisted in field-testing Conibear's traps.

Trapping seasons are monitored by the provincial Wildlife Branch and annual records are maintained of the fur harvest of every licenced trapper in the province.

British Columbia is also among the leaders in trapper education because humane trapping involves, not only the types of trap used, but also the technique employed. Before a person can obtain a trapper's licence, he must earn the privilege by taking a three-day trapping course which places heavy emphasis on humane trapping and, as a conservation measure, proper handling of animal pelts in order to reduce waste through spoilage of valuable skins.

The anti-trapping sentiments are incomprehensible to most trappers. Having destroyed the sealing industry on the east coast, the often radical animal rights activists would like to stop all trapping. Such people would stop the fur industry, the industry that provided the foundation of Canada. Totally ignored is the 2,000,000-year evolution of mankind as a predatory animal, with a conscience and the desire to conserve creatures that share the environment with him. Not the least of these is the modern trapper.

Here is the story of one trapper.

Norman Mackenzie:
The Kahntah River Trapper

Norm Mackenzie of Fort St. John not only typifies but far exceeds the qualities common to many of the old-time wilderness trappers. He was three years old when his parents homesteaded in the Peace River country in 1920, and he has been part of that historic region of the old fur trade ever since.

Norman began his successful trapping career before he started school. With the arrival of trapping season each year, young Norm became busy with the trapping of weasels, squirrels and muskrats. During one of his early school years, he made more from his furs than his dad did from the farm. He was only sixteen when he put in his first full season trapping. At that time, muskrats averaged 45 cents, squirrels 10 cents, and a good weasel earned him a "whole dollar." By the time he registered a trapline in the 1930's, on the Kahntah River, 150 miles north of his home, Norman was an experienced trapper.

In 1939, Norm took his young wife, Iva, with him to the trapline. Following an early snow in the first week of November, they began the long journey on foot with their team of three good-sized dogs pulling a toboggan. They travelled light, with limited utensils and supplies, and only one small tarpaulin for overnight shelter. They spent six months on the trapline and then, in May, they took six days to walk out with their furs.

In 1979, Norm wrote a book, *The Law of Trap and Fang*, based on his experiences on the trapline. He describes the day-to-day life and work of a trapper in an interesting manner with many humorous sidelights. The central theme is about Norm's confrontations with a lone timber wolf that robbed his furs, escaped from a trap, killed one of his dogs, and generally led him a merry chase. Because the wolf was a stubborn and cagey old animal, Norm and Iva named him Winston for the great British prime minister.

Norm's sense of humour is further illustrated in his story about smoking out a black bear and the description of his petite wife dressing out a moose. One of his accounts describes what happened when he and Iva cut some aspen trees beside the creek in front of their cabin. Norm cut up the trees and Iva neatly stacked the green wood beside the cabin to dry out and then carried the branches down to the stream for the beavers to eat. On a return trip Norm and Iva found a well-padded trail from the cabin down to the water's edge. The beaver had methodically removed every green block of wood from beside the cabin and packed them back to the stream. Norm made a remark that the beaver had lost their lunch and came to the cabin to retrieve it.

Norm and his wife were attached to their sleigh and pack dogs which contributed no end to their trapping success. Norm says that if he were young again he would still use dogs.

Like so many wilderness trappers, Norm has experienced the periodic die-off of thousands of snowshoe hares infected with disease and the subsequent starvation of lynx and other furbearers resulting from the decline in the food supply. This experience, like that of so many trappers, has made him an outspoken advocate of the importance of trapping and good wildlife management. He is a critic of animal-rights proponents who would stop all trapping and turn their backs on the waste of animals that die a lingering death from disease and starvation when their numbers exceed the carrying capacity of their environment.

Although Norm no longer works his trapline, his concern for good wildlife management and his interest in the affairs of trappers keep him active. He contributes regularly to the B.C. Trappers' Magazine, attends all the conventions, continues to express his concerns about anti-trapping sentiments, and has helped organize the Fort St. John trappers' local of which he was president for some years. He has been a director of the British Columbia Trappers' Association and for many years its vice-president. He is still an active Trapper Education Instructor and very much a proponent of good fur management.

Norm's dedication to the trapping industry and his appreciation for our natural resources is summarized in his statement: "I would like to impress on the public the great need we have for good wildlife management and the value of the trapper in the field."

"The buck stepped mincingly away from the cottonwoods, out into the water. The gun eased into my shoulder. But I didn't touch off the trigger, not while he was knee-deep in water. Having satisfied his thirst the buck stood there, staring off into space and thinking about things that buck deer usually think about when they're standing out in the water. It seemed a pity to shoot such a harmless and graceful fellow as he, but if I didn't shoot him, who knows, maybe tomorrow night a timber wolf or coyote might snuff out his life. And we needed the meat mortal bad."

Eric Collier
Three Against The Wilderness

Despite the wealth of wildlife that flourishes in British Columbia today, the earliest traders found local food supplies to be hard come by. Though they came for furs they traded for food. Crops were uncertain and their own hunting was not as productive as the need required. Wildlife and fish sustained them during those early years.

The settlers quickly learned the value of wildlife as well as the problems of supply posed by animal migrations and fluctuations. As settlements developed and farms became productive total dependency on wildlife decreased but the need never really vanished. There are families in British Columbia today who value highly the game on the table. It has been a staple food item for them for generations.

As times changed the availability of game became more restricted. Market hunting was outlawed. The only way to get wild meat was to hunt it yourself or have it given to you. Or buy it illegally. The common property resource became the consumable resource of only those who could hunt it in the field. And the numbers of those is dwindling.

In recent years the idea of game farming has been raised and partially rejected. It is almost certain to be raised again with the desire of some for a broader range of "farmed" game animals. Most British Columbians are no longer close to the land and its wildlife bounty; most do not need wild meat "mortal bad," as Collier did, but a good many would still like to have it available in some legitimate way. Legislators already face the interesting and complex social problem over the use of wildlife, the resource that sustained our earliest settlers.

CHAPTER 2

Wildlife — Our Talent of Silver

David R. Hurn

Any consideration of the wildlife resources of British Columbia such as were found by the first exploring Europeans is enhanced by a brief review of some of the political and cultural circumstances which prevailed in Europe and the Americas in 1700.

On the eve of the Industrial Revolution, the technologies of oceanic travel were reaching a very high state. Secondly, social evolution and economic vitality were contributing to unprecedented demands for raw materials and trade goods and, thirdly, the immensity of American lands was seen as relief for the agrarian needs of European people.

The consequent exploration and colonization of the land mass now known as British Columbia were the result of these three thrusts, which were manifest in accelerating European nationalism, aggressive commercial opportunism, and geographic and scientific enquiry.

Early in the eighteenth century, Spain was well established in Central America and up the west coast of North America to California. France and Britain remained in contested occupation of eastern North America and the Russians held a thin beachhead on the coast of the Alaskan peninsula down to the Nass River. The Portugese had confined their American adventures to the southern continent, while the Dutch, heavily committed in the Indian and western Pacific areas, showed little interest in the Americas.

Only scattered information and navigational records were available from previous Spanish and Russian sorties to these western shores when Captain James Cook, for Great Britain, undertook his third world-girdling voyage of discovery. His prime commission was to conclude historic speculation about a northern sea route from Europe to the Indies. Additionally, he was to provide dimension and shape to the northwest coast of North America and to gain knowledge of the people and resources of those lands. Cook's vessels were well-found and heavily stocked in preparation for very extensive voyages. Their travel strategy assumed that much of the fresh food necessary for his crews, and the livestock carried, would be obtained from the native inhabitants of the lands visited, by trading in manufactured goods. Indeed, Captain Cook and company sustained themselves royally in that portion of their Pacific voyage in New Zealand and the other islands of Polynesia.

At length, in March, 1778, Cook arrived off the Oregon coast, turned north-westward and followed the coast where, twenty days later, he put ashore at Nootka, on the midwest coast of Vancouver Island. There they found good anchorage and friendly natives, but only moderate trading opportunities for fur, hides and fish, and few of the fresh vegetables so needed by ocean travellers. Skins of bear, wolf, fox, deer, raccoon, polecat, marten and sea otter were obtained in trade with the Indians, as were several kinds of fish, but the travellers were not able to obtain wild meat or birds. This episode at Nootka was Cook's only landing in British Columbia. He later entered the Bering Sea from which his hunters took walruses from icepans for fresh meat.

Maritime traders followed James Cook: Spaniards, other British, New Englanders and Russians, all avid to promote trade in sea otter skins for the wealthy Oriental market. These sailors, whose commerce was with outer coast natives, were not well-supplied with local wildlife or plant foods, but they did fare well in fish, the common food of the coastal Indians.

After several years of diplomatic sparring, the long simmering conflict between the Spaniards, who had originally established an occupation at Nootka in 1774, and Britain, which held more military access, was settled by treaty. Captain George Vancouver, RN, was sent forth in 1792 to take possession of the Spanish installations at Nootka for the British Crown. Before proceeding to Nootka to execute that diplomatic mission, Vancouver conducted a most exact exploration of the continent's edge from Cape Disappointment, near the mouth of the Columbia River, round through the Strait of Juan de Fuca, Puget Sound, Georgia Strait, the mid-coastal inlets, and Queen Charlotte Sound. This venture, like those of Captain Cook before him, was well-found and fully victualled, but the need to obtain local products, meat and vegetables, was a requirement of such marine exploration. Vancouver carried crew members, referred to as "sportsmen," who had special responsibilities for hunting wildlife to supply the ships with fresh meat. They knew beforehand what animals were likely to be encountered, but they were limited in regular supply by confinement to the edge of the sea in locations dictated by requisites of safe anchorage rather than those of animal abundance. Venison (deer) and fish were obtained by trading with Indians, but the exchange was not brisk. In numerous locations, extensive side journeys were made in small boats into confined waters such as Hood Canal. They fished with hook and line and frequently employed beach seines to satisfy food needs. Additionally, they gathered "mussels, clams, cockles, nettle samphire and other coarse vegetables that had been so highly essential to our health and maintenance in all our former excursions." In that month of May, 1792, they saw numerous waterfowl in the inner waters of Puget Sound but, in spite of that promise of plenty, made note of their disappointment in meeting native people at Kingston, south of Port Townsend. "Their merchandise would have been infinitely more valuable to us had it been comprised of eatables, such as venison, wildfowl or fish, as our sportsmen and fishermen had little success in these pursuits." On Vashon Island, their hunters killed a buck which brought "relief" to their needs. Days later, they traded a "small copper for a whole deer." Still later, in Knight Inlet, well up-coast, an area not now known as a populous habitat for deer, the massed band of hunters was able to obtain, by shooting, several buck deer which exposed themselves on that vertical shore.

Cook and Vancouver, renowned as navigators and diplomats, are marked "special" in the annals of man, but they were merely mortal in the conversion of natural produce to satisfy the needs of their crews. They were not able to ensure a steady supply of fresh produce by their own hands. Rather, what little they did get by trading with natives reflected both the natural availability of game animals and birds and the food preferences of the Indians with whom they came in contact. Their successors in exploration of the wildlife wonders of British Columbia soon followed in increasing numbers over the next sixty years on both land and sea. They, too, were to learn that the Indian people, knowing the habits, location, and seasonal behaviour of wildlife, were the best sources of food.

Another measure of the fast developing maturity of nations was the rapidity with which the exploratory and scientific accomplishments of one nation were shared with the world community. James Cook had some records of the Danish Vitus Bering and his explorations for Russia, of the Asian-American interface. Similarly, Captain Cook knew of earlier Spanish voyages up the American coast (even though he failed to find the Strait of Juan de Fuca!). By such communications, Alexander Mackenzie was, by 1793, in possession of Cook's journals. Mackenzie knew the westerly limits of North America beyond the mountains. He knew where he was, and where he was to go. All that remained was to find a way over the Rocky Mountains, so long an obstacle to the bold activities of the North West Company, concerned almost singly in the commercial exploitation of wildlife for its skins.

Mackenzie, already a seasoned explorer of the northwest and a senior trader of "the Company," commenced his epic journey to the Pacific from a post on the western prairies in early May, 1793. By canoe, up the Peace River, they carried food staples, including pemmican, and trading goods sufficient to meet their needs over the "three moons" trip to the ocean. Like the marine explorers before them, they would need a steady supply of wild meat and plant food to sustain them.

The early upriver days through the Alberta portion of the Peace presented few surprises. The going was slow as a result of spring freshets, but the surrounding country swarmed with buffalo and elk (bison and wapiti). Near the mouth of the Pouce Coupe river, their hunters, especially adept at reading the sign and tracking game, killed two elk and wounded a buffalo from a concentration of animals termed "crowded." Similarly, several days later elk and buffalo were seen "in great abundance" near the mouth of the Beatton River, near Fort St. John. As the party moved upstream, the Peace River parklands yielded to continuous forest and, with that transition, sightings and acquisition of game rapidly lessened. Near Hudson Hope, the company hunters killed a small elk and wounded a "stag," here the first reference to another kind of deer in the journal. Wolves bothered the travellers encamped near the mouth of the Nation River. Mackenzie and his company then turned south and proceeded up the Parsnip River. They had, to that point, encountered few natives, whose presence was valued for trading purposes and as sources of geographical information on the path ahead. By June 5, in the vicinity of Anzac, they "had not seen even a partridge throughout the day, and the tracks of reindeer were of an old date." This is the first journal reference to caribou, similar to the Arctic variety, so well known to Mackenzie from his earlier journey to the northern ocean. At the divide between the Parsnip and the Fraser, after a meal of porcupine, they encountered a small group of Sekani Indians with whom they traded some of their precious pemmican for a few beaver skins and dried trout. The company men were perplexed at the origin of the dressed moose skins which the Indians possessed, because they had not, to this point, encountered evidence of this ungulate on this voyage.

Passing down the MacGregor River, a tributary of the Fraser River, they killed ducks and geese, and saw "swans in great numbers." On the same day, they found the horn of a goat, another first reference. The party reached the Fraser and, after taking some geese at the mouth of the MacGregor, continued downstream. Below where Prince George now lies (they missed the mouth of the Nechako River tributary!), they killed one of two "red deer," sighted on the bank. This reference to the European red deer species is thought to be a confusion with the summer colour phase of the mule deer, so common to the interior plateau of British Columbia and along much of the length of the Fraser River. Of these animals, Mackenzie wrote, "they are not so large as the elk of the Peace River, but are the real Red deer which I never saw in the north, though I have been told they are to be found in great numbers in the plains along the Red and Assiniboine Rivers."

Further onwards, near the present city of Quesnel, Indians told them that the country below abounded in animals and the river had plenty of fish, while, to the west, the Blackwater River country, "abounded in red deer and some of a small fallow kind."

On 23 June, 1793, after counsel with the Indians, the North West Company party abandoned the Fraser and prepared to head west, favouring foot passage to Bella Coola over the dangers of the canyons of the lower Fraser, further south. They turned back upstream, gaining the tributary Cottonwood canyon, where "our hunters returned but had not seen the tracks of any animal!" Proceeding westerly after caching their canoes, they met an Indian whose dress was trimmed with strips of sea otter fur, obtained from coastal Indians. Later, meeting natives of the Bella Coola valley, the Company men were trading for skins of otter, marten, bear, lynx and dressed moose skins, the last having been obtained by these people from the mountain Indians back to the northeast. These people possessed iron implements, reflecting some experience in trade with Europeans.

In Mackenzie pass "our hunters brought a small doe of the reindeer species — from a herd of them." "We stopped to dress some of our venison — that we made a heartier meal than we had done for many a day before." On their final outward leg to the sea, they saw, in North Bentinck Arm, a great number of sea otters. The party then headed back, carrying supplies of dried fish obtained from the Bella Coola Indians. They recovered their canoes and retraced their steps with greater food gathering success than earlier experienced. They consumed not only wild game found along the way but also stocks of pemmican and other basics, prudently cached on their outward trip. On reaching the pass in the Peace, their sightings of elk and buffalo increased and "moose deer" were seen for the first time.

In the five decades which followed Mackenzie's journey to the Pacific, much of the area of British Columbia was travelled, its human resources catalogued, and its natural resources, especially fur and salmon, were brought under exploitation for trade.

Simon Fraser followed Mackenzie's course through the Rockies, but, while he endured the perilous course of the Fraser river to its mouth at Musqueam (Point Grey), he concluded that the river was unsuitable as an avenue of transport and trade.

David Thompson crossed the Rockies at the headwaters of the Athabasca River into the Columbia drainage and, in the following decade, vigorously exploited trading opportunities with native people throughout the Kootenay, Snake, Pend Oreille, Spokane, Okanagan and Kettle river drainages.

During these and like expeditions of the fur traders, the voyageurs anticipated living off the land, either by the fruits of their own hunting and gathering, or by trade with the native people. They were frequently hungry. Often they saw edible wildlife but were unable to secure any and, indeed, their journals often report incidents such as, "we had our first fresh meat in days" after the gift of a marmot by friendly Indians. Scott and Hanic, writing in *East Kootenay Chronicle* said, "one thinks of the Kootenay country of this period (1808) as teaming with game and the rivers practically clogged with fish. But the early explorers did not find it so. By May, 1808, Thompson's party was almost starving. After going without food for several days, they found an eagle feeding on the carcass of an antelope" — and they ate the remains! But when Thompson camped above Toby Creek at Kootenay House he found an abundance of game.

The history of the expansion of the fur trade into British Columbia is replete with names and odysseys of travel into unknown lands, journeys which are now legendary. Passage by canoe on the riverine highways was "the way to go" in those days, but it was not a travel mode which provided the food and maintenance needs of the travellers. They were tolerant men, upholding trading policies of their companies, by which civil relations with native peoples were established and maintained, thereby enabling the traders to stay alive and prosper in their commercial ventures.

By 1825, the fur companies had consolidated their territories and trading relations in south and central British Columbia. Trading posts were built and manned at Fort St. James (1806), Fort George (1807), Fort Thompson (1812), Forts Connally and Chilcotin (1826). Similar outposts were secured on the Columbia at Fort Spokane, Fort Colville and Fort Vancouver, near the mouth of the Columbia. These scattered settlements were initially sustained by the traditional canoe routes from central Canada. Staffs of these outposts, while supplied with some basic foods, nevertheless remained dependent on local wild foods. Crops were planted for seasonal supply, and hunting opportunities were pursued, but foods obtained from natives continued to be their principal source. The paradox of wildlife abundance became known to these first white settlers, as it did to Thompson in 1808, who quickly came to appreciate the significance of the horizontal and vertical migrations of our larger ungulates and predators, and of the immense impact that winters had upon the subsequent availability of the larger mammals. "Life was hard for them, especially during the first year when starvation threatened and the Blackfoot Indians plagued them," a note by Clara Graham in *This Was the Kootenay*, about life at Kootenay House trading post at Lake Windermere in 1807.

In 1821, the Hudson's Bay Company merged with the Northwest Company, vesting in the Hudson's Bay Company exclusive trading rights to all British lands north of the Columbia River. Up to this time virtually every person of European stock in British Columbia was in service to "the Company." Further consolidation of operations was achieved with the beginnings of trade supply by sea, through Fort Vancouver on the lower Columbia River. By this means, livestock was introduced for use at trading outposts and this shift in supply came to have great significance, not only to the security of Company operations, but to the settlement opportunities which were soon to follow. Immediately, of course, the feast-and-famine economy of wild ungulates as necessary food was damped, and dried fish quickly became an item of export.

American and British skirmishes in the Oregon territory were finally dispersed with the signing of the Boundary Treaty. All Hudson's Bay Company operations were moved north of the 49th parallel and staffs therefrom relocated to established, or new outposts, in British Columbia. This was the origin of Fort Camosun and lesser, shortlived posts at Fort Simpson and Fort McLaughlin in the Skeena country. The stage was set for change, and it came rapidly, as a result of a political condition imposed on the charter of the Company, stipulating that it must develop opportunity for settlement, a condition initially met reluctantly by the Hudson's Bay Company.

Thus ended the exploratory era in which the "where is it?" "who's in it?' and "what's in it?' questions were largely answered. Fur was still the basis of the territory's economy. Wildlife remained a necessary item of food for both natives and company settlers. Marine trading routes, linking Company posts with Britain and California greatly enriched the trading potential in a still-thin land. The sooth "Go West Young Man" gave a new meaning to British Columbia's development with the discovery of gold in California in 1849. Then, the political stage having been set with the formation of local government in British Columbia, it happened! Gold was discovered on the bars of the Fraser, and the effect upon the wildlife resources of the territory, now a Crown Colony, was notably shifted. Dreams of opportunity of settlement in a new, rich land were married with the golden chance of instantaneous wealth, the common consequence of which was an inpouring of people to the Colony. The basic supporting infrastructure serving both the trader-colonist and the gold seekers was in place: wealth came with them as did the cultural institutions of their home lands. The miners had no time to hunt moose or deer or catch fish — gold was their game. The wealth they generated enabled them to buy their food — at some cost, from coastal and newly formed interior sources. Traders of a new sort, and settlers intent on mining bovine gold from vacant grasslands, rapidly developed trade routes and supply — all of which was accomplished with remarkably little drain on the wildlife resources of the Fraser basin.

Elsewhere, permanent colonization proceeded quite unrelated to the fur economy of the previous fifty years. People came by sea from Great Britain, from the western United States and overland from upper Canada. By 1865, settlement and supply centres were in evidence on Vancouver Island, the Fraser Valley, the Kootenay, Okanagan, and Thompson valleys, and along Barnard's road to Barkerville. Agricultural business began and, with it, reduced demand for wildlife, whether fur, meat or other wild products. With the erasure of exclusive trading privilege, the profile of the Hudson's Bay Company was trimmed and the Indian people lost their privileged position as procurers of native goods.

There followed a period of about 60 years in which the present settlement pattern of the province was established. As they came and spread, the settlers cleared land and raised crops and stock. So, too, grew commercial systems of supply and service, many of which persist to this day.

Still, life was not easy. Cash was in short supply and the settlers took wild food from the fields, forests, ponds and beaches. Historian B. Norcross noted that, "what appeared on the table was very largely limited to what the country provided. There was plenty of game and, for those who lived near the sea, clams in abundance."

Tales of the Windermere tells us of the homesteader, Marigeau: "When Baptiste wanted meat for the table, he had only to step to the door of their home in the early morning or evening and wait. Deer and elk were never far off, and a single shot could provide dinner for many days (1880)." The Cornwall brothers, whose ranch was established at Hat Creek in 1862 to supply miners and travellers, "kept busy cutting fence posts and rails, hunting, playing cards and reading. Deer, rabbits and prairie chicken were plentiful." In a similar vein, Hazel Hill, writing of the early days said, "The Alberni Valley was simply swarming with game. Ducks, geese, blue and willow grouse, bears, cougar and wolves were plentiful. Deer were everywhere and there were elk in some valleys. Wolves were a problem then to the early farmers."

Father Morice, that rare cleric historian, records that "most of those lakes and rivers contained excellent fish. These sheets of water become also annually the rendezvous of myriads of duck, geese and other aquatic fowls which, as the grible (sic) abound to such an extent that for a fortnight or so, they are daily taken by the hundred in a single locality."

The family of Charles De B. Green, settlers at Osoyoos, was "seldom without game. Blue and willow grouse, ducks, hares and prairie chicken all being plentiful in those days." Lieutenant-Colonel Peters, in his report of 1897, noted in his assessment of the military position of the province that Nelson, a community of 2,000 persons and rapidly increasing, "is absolutely unarmed. This section of the country is quite devoid of game so no one keeps arms about their homes."

As late as 1910, the Vancouver Island Development Association wrote, in describing the agricultural potential of the southernmost districts of Vancouver Island that, "the appearance of deer is more familiar to them than many a rancher would wish. Venison, however, makes a welcome change in the diet of the settler." In respect to sheep raising, "the principal drawback is the mountain lion, or panther, whose occasional ravages are responsible for a loss of perhaps 5%. It affords excellent sport to local hunters who seldom fail to bag the destroyer."

Denman Island, settled in the 1860's, "had a good population of deer." Wallace Baikie, in his recall of early days on the Island wrote, "When the early settlers needed meat for the table they would go out and shoot a deer; however during the daylight hours, it took time to hunt down a deer, so instead of wasting daylight hours, they would go hunting in the backfield with a pit lamp."

Even as late as the nineteen twenties and thirties, lands were still being settled by latter-day pioneers. English immigrant Eric Collier wrote in his narrative, *Three Against The Wilderness* that when they moved to Meldrum Creek, "We had to live off the woods, and if they hadn't much to offer, they were generous with what they had. Deer were not only to furnish us meat but clothing too of sorts." Collier exclaimed that it was years before store-bought lard replaced the fat of fall bear in their kitchen.

From 1860 onwards, populations swelled and commerce expanded, lands were cleared and cropped and villages and cities developed. The economy of the province shifted from fur to agriculture, fishing and mining. Soon there were city folk providing all manners of service and trade and, on the land, the farmers. The Indian people, so long upheld in the position of privileged purveyor of fur, wildlife and fish, were abandoned to the rigours of the marketplace.

Firearms, now in common distribution, were in this period greatly improved and commonly obtained. Bag limits, seasons and other forms of control upon hunting were few and primitive. Conversion of wild land to agriculture, and forest removal, while of local significance to wildlife abundance, had not so progressed as to have by then created a troublesome paucity of game in any quarter of the province. The tradition of subsistence on wildlife, whether taken by oneself, or by the hand of a market hunter, became culturally imprinted upon the settlers, whether of early Canadian, United States or British origin. The demand for wild meat increased, as did the by-products, such as hides and feathers.

Blanche Norcross, in her history of the Cowichan Valley, *The Warm Land*, wrote, "Hunting was a combination of business and pleasure. A man could not only supply his own table while getting some sport, but he could make a little cash in Victoria by the sale of fresh venison or grouse." Similarly John Cherrington, in his look back at *Mission on the*

Fraser said, "Every Saturday was market day. At Catherwood's Hatzic General Store, one could always hear the local gossip. The store stocked basic provisions such as sugar, flour and salt. But Catherwood seemed to do his best business with hunters. Men brought him grouse, ducks and fish, which he bought and then shipped by daily steamer to New Westminster (1908)."

From an earlier day, Edgar Fawcett, writing about Victoria in the 1860's, made reference to Christmas preparations of those days: "Turkey might not have been within their reach, but geese, wild or tame, took the place." "The Songhee Indians would sell at your door grouse and ducks at 35 to 50 cents a pair, venison by the quarter at 5 to 8 cents a pound, a salmon at 10 cents and oysters for 25 cents a bucket."

Later, the Weaver brothers of Ladner, well-known market gunners, sustained a supply of several dozen ducks or geese twice a week to Adams' store in New Westminster. One year (c. 1895) Harry shot 1,800 ducks — a brace of mallards fetched 40 cents, pintails 35 cents and 25 cents for teal. Brant or geese were 75 cents. Waterfowl numbers in the Fraser lowlands were, before the draining of Sumas lake, and the extensive conversions to farmland, simply tremendous. Harry Weaver on one occasion, with eight hunters, took turns shooting from a single blind and picked up 128 brant in a few hours. Another recollection, recorded by Barry Leach, and quoted in his *Waterfowl on a Pacific Estuary*, was that, "In a good year he (Franklin) and a companion sold 2,500 brant to Pat Burns and Company before New Year's Day," and "Market hunters on Vancouver Island and the lower mainland were especially busy in December shooting large numbers of brant for sale at Christmas — when they fetched 50 cents a brace." It was, of course, not long before the steady drain of market hunting began to hit upon animal abundance. There were, in addition to the rapid conversions of land to uses alien to wildlife, abuses of animal slaughter which even they, pioneers of a land and a time in which wildlife was a common denominator of living, could not abide.

A. Bryan Williams, one of the province's earliest wildlife officials wrote in his *Game Trails in British Columbia* that the drybelt of British Columbia "simply swarmed" with mule deer, but that their numbers had greatly declined. "The decrease was brought about in many ways, but the start began when market hunters slew them solely for their hides. At one time there was an almost constant stream of wagons passing from the Okanagan Valley across the line into the United States, and their sole freight consists of mule deer skins." The sum of pressures, the gun and the plow, the saw and the cow, the dam and the ditch, eventually provoked a movement to protect the shrinking bounty of wildlife. Seasons for hunting were applied, which foretold of the end of market hunting for upland birds and ungulates, although it was not until well into the twentieth century that commerce was finally terminated.

Wildlife conservation pressures were growing in the province. A shift to affluent security caused the importation of a number of alien animals and birds, well-known as sporting species in Europe or Britain. These animals, secured at some cost and representing high expectation for sport, were given hitherto unheard-of protection.

The final (almost) phase of market hunting in British Columbia continued until the province fully joined with Canada in the 1916 treaty on Migratory Birds, which, by 1922, put "paid" on the sale of ducks, geese, swans, pigeons and other wildfowl.

There are pockets of settlement in British Columbia where there persists the pioneer notion of untrammelled public right to use wildlife for subsistence. Until the middle 1960's, a "free miner's" permit to take wildlife for food was available to bona fide prospectors in British Columbia — a subsidy by the Crown to assist mineral exploration.

Today, commercial use of wildlife in British Columbia is confined to wild fur harvest and the recreational marketing of wildlife consumption under the regulation of the provincial and federal governments.

In the span of two hundred years, this incredibly varied land has been diminished from a fertile environment to which was adapted in almost every niche a marvellous array of wild animals, birds and fish. Wildlife was the first wealth which drew Europeans and a few Asiatics to this province. It was the resource that literally sustained them, as explorers and settlers, and was the economic means by which they generated capital to lead to a more secure and prosperous life.

It is both unlikely and undesirable that wildlife will ever again form the basis of man's food needs in British Columbia. Wild ungulates, and birds, so long as they remain wild, no longer constitute a dependable food source, and certainly not one which could sustain a population of almost three million people, the majority of whom live urban lives removed from wildlife and natural environments. Many, however, continue to "use" wildlife as a study of wilderness, together with plants and trees, landforms and waterways, and all their ecological associations. Still, a few people, living on the land, or who return to it, hunt for recreation under rigid controls. Like the trappers, they are reminded by their closeness to wildlife that it was the beaver, the deer, the grouse and duck, the otter and the salmon, which made it possible for all of us to be here today. Let us ensure that, by good husbandry, wildlife will be with us tomorrow.

"Under our parliamentary system, a Prime minister or a Premier with a majority has immense power... In 1688 we traded the divine right of kings for the divine right of a Premier... with a majority...

"So when there is no action at all by a government that has a majority, then that's clearly because they don't want to act. If they do want to act, the whole matter is relatively simple."

Hon. John Fraser, 1981
Roundtable Discussion on Toxic
Chemical Laws and Policy in Canada

It has long been a truism among wildlife managers that their art is not one of handling animals but of managing people. This became more and more difficult as populations grew, as they congregated in cities, as their understanding of the natural world seemed diminished, and as their ability to kill or otherwise affect wildlife grew out of proportion to their understanding of what they were doing.

Early man, here as elsewhere, was limited by the inefficiencies of his technology in his capacity to seriously destroy wildlife or its habitat. Even the Indians who burned the prairies could not destroy the vast herds of buffalo. But as technology improved so did the capacity to chase and kill animals. This, coupled with a growing demand for wildlife and wildlife parts, compelled governments to enact legislation for the protection of wildlife.

Often this was done on a hit-or-miss basis, influenced by various interest groups, and always subject to the particular philosophy of the government in power. It hardly needs saying that some governments are reluctant to pass or enforce regulations that inhibit peoples' ability to exercise their own free will. Other governments control people by regulation because they fear that an unregulated populace will run amok. The search for a middle ground in governing has always remained difficult.

Notwithstanding the difficulty, laws have been passed, and wildlife has been protected; not always wisely or on time, but adequately in the long run. Governments' ability to pass appropriate legislation is bounded only by its inability to gain credibility with the public through communication and consultation.

CHAPTER 3

Wildlife and the Law

Donald J. Robinson

All societies have ways and means to distribute use of resources needed for their survival and wildlife was important to the survival of British Columbia's aboriginal people. Its use was critical during the pre-European period, economically valuable during the early colonization era and has increased in worth throughout recent settlement and development of the province of British Columbia. The role of wildlife has changed over the past two centuries as the indigenous culture was modified and then succeeded by European attitudes. But some of the original attitudes about wildlife were never extinguished and are part of today's mosaic of wildlife use.

It is generally accepted that, prior to the arrival of Europeans, native people had developed a form of land tenure that provided a base for controlled use of fish, plants and wildlife required for their existence. Although the influence of bands and tribes rose and fell over the millenia, the arrangement allowed for a form of ownership or monopoly over the wildlife resources inhabiting an area. Such rights were usually handed down from one generation to the next, providing for continuity of control and use. They also provided for intertribal trade, so that scarce commodities such as caribou hides and fish oil could be widely distributed. Custom in some tribes allowed hunting and fishing territories to be bought or rented, although regulation of the harvest appeared to reside with the monopolistic right of the owner.

Essentially, the pre-European Indian cultures relied on various forms of monopolistic land tenure and resource-use rights to regulate the use of wildlife. These rights were usually vigorously defended but in some cases could be sold or rented out.

European influence upon native culture began in earnest in 1785 when James Hanna, the first British trader, arrived on the west coast of Vancouver Island to take up the sea otter trade. Hanna's arrival as a trader intent on developing the fur trade followed and probably resulted from the earlier discoveries of Captain James Cook. Coastal Indians rapidly became part of the trading operation as it furnished many trade items of a new technology. The rapid exploitation of the sea otter brought near extirpation by the mid-1800's and the exchange of goods dwindled. By 1804, however, land-based traders had reached the Peace River area in their avid search for fur, especially beaver, and a more lasting trade arrangement was started.

The impact of the new fur trade caused erosion of tribal tenure laws as a result of competition from trappers, often "foreign" Indians, as well as Europeans. The stable and monopolistic type of wildlife tenure was being eroded.

The Hudson's Bay Company, throughout most of its trade area, had imposed by 1822 restrictive regulations such as a ban against buying summer-killed beaver and the sale of steel traps. These were measures designed, to be sure, to increase the value of animals taken, although the ban on steel traps resulted from their unselective action, as compared to traditional Indian methods. In 1826, the Hudson's Bay Company brought in beaver pelt quotas for fourteen districts. While this may not have applied to British Columbia, it is strong evidence that the company was able to impose conservation regulations when they would benefit the fur resource, ultimately improving profits.

The Hudson's Bay Company during the four or five decades prior to the founding of the colony of British Columbia in 1858 practiced a monopolistic control over the wildlife resources of value to the company. This monopoly applied over a large area and was effective in maintaining a steady supply of furs and other wildlife products, in spite of fluctuations of numbers of fur-bearers and the market. In some respects it was similar to the monopolistic land tenure and associated rights to wildlife and fish practiced by most Indian bands. It obviously was superimposed upon the aboriginal system, to protect the Company's interest.

This fairly steady policy of regulating the use of wildlife for livelihood and commerce came to an abrupt end in 1858 when the Hudson's Bay Company lost its exclusive Indian trade in British Columbia with the founding of the new colony of British Columbia. Free enterprise became the order of the day and the resources became available for development under new laws and regulations. The game resource ceased to be treated as a monopoly by the Hudson's Bay Company and Indian bands and, instead became a common property resource, available to everyone. No doubt Europeans had utilized game since their first arrival as a matter of need but now this use could be extended and carried out under new attitudes translated into western law.

It did not take the colonial government long to recognize the need for game laws. On April 20, 1859, barely a year after its founding, the House of Assembly, under Speaker J. S. Helmcken, passed an Act Providing for the Preservation of Game. This initial act had a preamble of value in understanding the thrust of the legislation. It is worth noting for its appreciation of the value of game and the need to protect it.

"Birds and beasts of game constitute an important source of food, and the pursuit thereof affords occupation, and means of subsistence to many persons in the Colony, as well as a healthy and manly recreation;

"And whereas the pursuit and destruction of game in the breeding season tends to the extinction of the whole race, and whereas game is unwholesome and unfit for food, and it is expedient to prohibit the destruction and use thereof in the breeding season..."

The preamble states game is an important source of food, has commercial value, provides a good form of recreation and needs protection under certain conditions. Other specific sections governed the period when game could not be bought or sold, provided penalties and administrative requirements for law enforcement, including issuance of summons and limitation of prosecution. This act set a simple but sound course as it recognized both commercial and non-commercial use of game and the need to protect stocks during the breeding season and initiated law enforcement procedures and brought the game resource under the active control of the colonial government.

Other amendments and ordinances were passed during the next 46 years to deal with increasingly complex problems. The following are noteworthy and demonstrate authority gradually being increased to manage the common property game resource including protection for non-game.

1870   This ordinance prohibited possession of game within one mile of Victoria, New Westminster, Nanaimo and Esquimalt or aboard any steamer between March 1st and August 10th and for venison (elk and deer) between February 1st and August 1st in any year. The definition of game included dead birds such as grouse, quail, pheasant, partridge, robin, lark, thrush and wild pigeon. But in 1872 pigeons were excluded from the provisions of the 1870 statute — we can only speculate on the reason.

1878   This legislation prescribed that deer, elk, reindeer, caribou and hare could be sold only during the open season and for three days after its end. It became illegal to hunt or take game with dogs during the closed season. Farmers could kill deer which were depasturing cultivated fields.

1887   Laws were passed outlawing the sale of pheasants at any time. Many species of birds were being introduced during this period and some, such as blackbirds, thrushes, linnets, skylarks and chaffinches were protected by law. Gulls were protected when in the harbours of Victoria, Esquimalt, New Westminster and Vancouver. Protection of the law was given to many birds, especially insectivorous species providing very early evidence that birds and mammals were valued for more than simple utilitarian use. Enforcement was strengthened when persons providing information leading to conviction were given moiety amounting to half the assessed fine.

1890 This amendment prohibited the use of dogs to hunt deer west of the Cascade Mountains. It also provided authority to take birds and their eggs for scientific and acclimatization purposes. Non-residents (except members of the armed services and the militia when on service in the province) were required to obtain a $50 licence to hunt. A licenced non-resident was allowed 10 deer, two bull elk, three reindeer, five caribou, eight sheep, and eight mountain goat. By 1905 this bag was somewhat reduced to 10 deer, three caribou, three mountain sheep, three mountain goat, two bull moose and two bull elk.

1895 Regulations further restricted the conditions under which game could be sold. Provision was made for Indians and settlers in unorganized districts to take game for their immediate and reasonable use for food only.

Gradually, over the period 1859 to 1904, legislation about the game resource was broadened to provide more specific authority. By and large, the changes and additions allowed for more ways and means to deal with problems, to protect game herds and to manage the increasingly complex ways that a growing population of people could interact with wildlife.

Land owners and farmers received protection from trespass and problem animals, bounties were paid, open and closed seasons were introduced, emergency season closures were possible, enforcement was provided with due process and significant fines and penalties were prescribed. These and many other minor but useful regulations soon built up a substantial body of law, but there was no single government agency having the sole responsibility for the game resource.

A growing number of sportsman's associations recognized this shortcoming and lobbied for a single agency to be responsible for the game resource through a revised game act. The government responded and in 1905 passed the Game Amendment Act which placed the responsibility for game in the Department for the Protection of Game and Forests under the direction of A. Bryan Williams, the first game and forest warden. The new act attempted to bring together in an orderly form the various changes and amendments that comprised the body of law about game and introduced some new ideas.

Mr. Williams was certainly the man for the task and served ably during his first term, which ended in 1918. The new act of 1905 was probably drafted in part by Mr. Williams. It dealt with issues that he constantly referred to during his term. The act was concerned with strengthening enforcement to prevent poaching, controlling out-of-province Indian hunting, restoring game herds, maintaining the economic return from trapping and guiding of non-residents, and providing recreation from hunting and fishing based on fair rules of chase.

Enforcement was carried out by the provincial police, aided by deputy wardens paid by the game associations of Victoria and Vancouver. Groups such as prospectors and surveyors, while working in the field, were allowed to kill game at any time of the year for personal use. This accommodation to frontier conditions existed until rescinded in 1966. The management of beaver, a mainstay of the fur industry, received closer scrutiny, resulting in a short general closure. A serious attempt was made to control the spring shooting of waterfowl, a provincial responsibility because in 1905 the Migratory Bird Convention Act was more than a decade away.

In 1910 the Game Branch was removed from the Department of Lands and Works and placed under the Attorney-General, where it stayed in one form or another for the next 47 years. During this period the influence of law and enforcement was central to the administration.

Over the next 13 years there were a number of useful additions to the Game Amendment Act of 1905. The first budget of $10,000 for game administration was passed in 1908. Although monies for bounties and other expenses had been paid out in previous years, the appropriation in 1908 was the first time funds were available in a separate vote, a practice continued to the present time. Resident hunting licences, a mainstay of all game departments, were imposed in 1913. This significant step produced substantial revenue (in excess of $110,000), increased enforcement capability, and provided a measure of public use of the resource. The first year's sales amounted to:

Ordinary Firearms Licence (deer and game birds)	$ 2.50	$27,724
General Firearms (all game, including big game)	5.00	2,527
Special Firearms Licence (trapping, all game)	10.00	1,707
Guide Licence	5.00	45
Free Licence to farmers, prospectors and surveyors	0	7,639 licences

Authorities had estimated about 12,000 licences would be issued, whereas nearly 40,000 were required. This surprising revenue allowed more staff to be hired and subsequently 26 deputy wardens were appointed. The large number of licences clearly indicated a high level of use and awareness of the game resource, especially the willingness to buy licences, which were costly, relative to wages of the day.

The licencing system involved more than just hunting. It incorporated the radical notion that one of the licences was "compulsory for everyone who carries firearms." The argument in favour of this approach was that game was recognized as valuable to the province, thus stronger game laws and stricter enforcement were necessary. But this required more funds. Although some people were benefiting from the resource they were contributing little to its upkeep. The direct user was deemed to be responsible for the greater share of protection costs. The direct user was judged to be at least all who carried firearms.

The combination of a firearms licence with a hunting licence stood until 1955, when a low-cost, separate carrying licence for firearms was instituted. British Columbia had the most rigorous firearm licencing system in Canada.

The first period of modern game administration ended in 1918 when the Game Department was abolished. Williams was retired and the responsibility for the Game Act placed under the Provincial Police. A Game Conservation Board was established consisting of five members under the leadership of Dr. A. R. Baker. The other members were the Curator of the Provincial Museum (Secretary), three members-at-large appointed by order-in-council and, ex-officio, the Chief Game Inspector. It was later expanded to 12 members to improve provincial representation but reports indicate it was too unwieldy. Because it was advisory, it had no power of implementation.

As usual, when the agency was being reorganized, the Act was amended. All provincial police became ex-officio game wardens. The list of protected species was expanded to include pigeons, doves, Western and American robins and thrushes. Farmers were entitled to hunt without licence only on their own property and "pit-lamping" became a prison offence, without option of a fine. Pit-lamping (hunting at night through the use of a miner's underground light) had become the most heinous of game offences. Why this is so is not reported but probably arises from the comparative ease of kill, the lack of ethics and the danger to domestic animals and humans.

Protection of the game resource, particularly furbearers, was paramount during the 1920's. A prohibition against placing of poison where it may cause damage to fur species was adopted in 1920 and continues to the present as a more restrictive regulation. A royalty on fur was introduced in 1926 in conjunction with a Fur Trader's licence at a cost of $20 for a resident trader and $200 for non-resident. The fur trader's licence provided a way to monitor the collection of the royalty, which had to be paid prior to the export of fur from the province. The enabling legislation for registering trap lines, adopted in 1923, was put into regulation and registration began. It was largely completed by 1934. This significant program provided some monopolistic rights to the registered owner, while retaining Crown control over the resource. Continuous unilateral use of the fur resource within a defined area was assured to the registered trapper, providing the use was consistent with government policy. This approach greatly reduced but did not eliminate trap line boundary disputes, which continue to this day. A complicating factor has been the transfer of trap lines, with agency consent, coincident with the sale of goods and equipment. This has made disputes more difficult to resolve, especially Indian trap line problems associated with comprehensive claims. The administrative record is usually over 50 years old and often broken and unclear.

From the late 1880's to the early 1900's, game associations took an active role in the management of game. While the close association appears to have continued with the agency under Bryan Williams, the associations reportedly were quite critical of the game administration under the provincial police from 1918 to 1929. Relationships are reported to have improved when Williams was recalled from retirement and appointed Game Commissioner. The Act was amended so that the game agency was separated from the provincial police, control removed from the Board and placed under the authority of the single Commissioner, Williams.

Williams served as the Commissioner until his second retirement in 1934. At that time a Game Commission was established comprised of James G. Cunningham, a former game inspector; Frank R. Butler, Secretary of the previous Board, and A. G. Bolton, a hatchery officer from Vancouver Island. Bolton soon retired but the Commission form of administration by Cunningham and Butler lasted until April, 1957, when it became part of the newly formed Department of Recreation and Conservation.

The use of a tagging system for deer was started in 1932 and, although modified many times, still remains. This regulation had a dual purpose: to raise revenue and to improve enforcement. Since then, tagging requirements have been applied to all big game species and, in addition to revenue and enforcement, have supplied the sampling base for harvest surveys. It is one of the more useful tools of management.

The interval between 1934 and 1944 was not noteworthy for major changes. There was a war on and enforcement and routine administration were the key activities. Gradually, the Game Act became a "thou shalt not" document, providing a strong base for enforcement. It also contained many complex administrative details about permits, forms, and licences required for the use and protection of the game resource. It was a conservative period.

Non-resident hunters multiplied rapidly after the war and trophy fees were increased to dampen the influx. Revenue increased, yet so did the number of non-resident hunters. Their demand for guide services, especially in the moose area of the south central plateau from Clinton to Quesnel, hindered the application of a guide registration system similar to trap lines. Instead, the high demand for guides led to the guide block option, wherein several guides operated in a large area. This lasted until the modern era for guiding began in 1969, when legislation provided options of the gradual dismantling of blocks by the guides themselves.

The first extensive cow moose season since the closure in 1892 occurred in 1952 with a six-day season in the south central portion of the province. This was followed by a doe season in 1953 for Sayward Forest on Vancouver Island, only four years after a complete closure to deer hunting to allow stocks to rebuild after two severe winters. And in 1954, bull elk were again legal quarry on Vancouver Island.

There were other changes. For example: in 1954 the Game Act was amended to legalize the taking of big game under one year of age. It appears the cow moose and doe deer seasons of preceeding years were probably illegal because juveniles were accidently taken. This simple change provided one of the cornerstones of intensive management, one that becomes increasingly valuable as population dynamics and modelling became central to management strategy.

In 1957 the Deptartment of Recreation and Conservation was created, which removed the responsibility for the fish and wildlife resources from a Commission under the Attorney-General and placed them in a department which combined resource management and amenity services. This marked the official recognition of wildlife as a renewable resource for the first time since 1910, when it had been placed with the provincial police, under the Attorney-General.

The formation of the Department of Recreation and Conservation also marked the end of the Conservation Fund, which had a short but useful existence. In 1950, then Attorney-General Gordon Wismer discussed at a public game convention an innovative funding process for the Game Commission. He called it the Conservation Fund. It was to provide a more stable funding base as well as encouraging planning for the management of fish and game. At the Game Convention of 1951 he outlined the new fund, which had just been approved by the Provincial Legislature. Essentially, 75 percent of revenues, including fines, were to be set aside in a special fund within Consolidated Revenue for use by the Game Commission, as approved by the Attorney-General. If budgetary expenditures were less than the 75 percent of revenues, the difference was to be maintained in the fund in a non-lapsing manner and be available for game and fish management. The fund was confirmed in 1954 when Mr. Wismer, under questioning, stated the Conservation Fund was provided by Statute and its use was not a matter of ministerial discretion. Again in 1956, the Attorney-General, then the Hon. Robert Bonner, reported the Game Conservation Fund had been heavily used over the past 16 months on special studies related to B.C. Hydro and other resource developments. But only one year later, at the 1957 game convention in Penticton, the Hon. E. C. Westwood, Minister of Recreation and Conservation, now responsible for the fish and wildlife resources, told the assembled delegates that the Game Conservation Fund had been put into General Revenue. The reasoning was that special funds should not be established, as all major expenditures must be voted upon during the legislative session. The B.C. Wildlife Federation campaigned vigorously against the loss but to no avail.

In 1964 the prohibition against the use of four-wheel-drive vehicles while hunting was deleted. This regulation had been imposed after the war, when large numbers of surplus jeeps and other vehicles became available at low prices. The debate over those vehicles centred on their ability to provide access to previously inaccessible areas. The prohibitionists were correct in their concern about improved access but the developing road systems built for the expanding logging and mining industries were the real problem. The Game Act of the time did not have power to control vehicle access so the alternative was to control hunting methods, such as the use of four-wheel-drive vehicles. Indeed, the impact of opening new areas was not clearly understood so this factor continued to mask local over-hunting for another decade or more.

The Game Act was replaced by a Wildlife Act in 1966 and certain sections dealing with firearms in a non-hunting mode were placed in a Firearms Act. This separated the two functions contained in hunting licences since their inception in 1913, while still retaining the same degree of control.

The review and drafting of the Wildlife Act provided the biologically trained managers their first opportunity to develop a Resource Management Act. The name of the act implied it would be concerned with a wider range of species than just game. Its thrust was to provide enabling legislation to meet the varying conditions, problems and opportunities found throughout the province. The licencing system was changed to a single licence as a prerequisite for species tag licences, which were to be introduced as required. This framework has served quite well and is in current use (1987). A decentralized or regional administration was set up so that programs and services could better serve local needs. Habitat for wildlife was recognized but little was done other than allowing purchase of land under the Act. This, however, was a significant new power. While enabling legislation sections provided for a great deal of flexibility in regulations about species and their use, the same cannot be said of habitat management. Water, land and forests were under strong unilateral acts and the time was not right for either providing the Wildlife Act with ways to interact with them or to have a provincial resource co-ordination act. Cougar and wolf were given game status. New

51

regulations such as three-quarter minimum curl on Rocky Mountain sheep, archery seasons and separate seasons for white-tailed deer and mule deer became possible.

The guiding regulations had long been recognized as needing revision to provide for better administration for a stronger industry. There had been amendments in 1948 providing for different classes of guide but the 1966 act contained wording to allow for much more significant changes. This option fostered negotiations between the Branch and guides, leading to new regulations in 1969. The regulations provided for an extended period of tenure, up to 15 years, through a certificate, providing the applicant had an exclusive territory with no boundary disputes with adjoining guides. The certified areas could be bought and sold, and so provided a strong stimulus for guides in blocks, or with overlaps, to work out solutions. By the early 1980's, most guides had certified territories, which provided them with an improved economic basis for their business. It helped the guiding industry become more resource conscious and more business oriented. It was a step similar to the registering of trap lines, as guides with certificates could sell their territory and had a monopoly to provide guiding services to non-residents, who were and still are required to use guides when hunting big game.

Enforcement was not overlooked. While this act stressed management of wildlife, there were significant enforcement advances. The wildlife ticket was introduced as a much simpler and less costly method of handling the more common and usually less serious infractions. It is similar to traffic tickets. Previously, all cases were handled through the court process, although there were some provisions for a guilty plea to be handled through a waiver. The ticket provides for a person entering a guilty plea to pay a pre-set fine without a court appearance. Of course, anyone wishing to plead not guilty had access to the courts.

In 1968 the Creston Valley Wildlife Management Area Act was passed. This extremely strong act established control over all activities on certain lands reserved for wildlife, particularly migratory birds. It is concerned mainly with management of land. It is an active act which includes many sections prescribing how to manage wildlife. It also re-established a Trust Fund based on income obtained from permits, licences and other fees established by the Management Authority, as well as bequests and gifts. The Fund can also receive the profit from enterprises undertaken by the authority. It marks the first time that wildlife was given paramountcy on a large tract of land and that funds derived other than from appropriations could be kept and used to further the area's needs. It is a form of free enterprise for wildlife, operating in a non-profit way under a strong act. This form of Crown corporation has worked well in attracting significant development funds from Ducks Unlimited, securing compensation from B.C. Hydro for using the area, and resisting attempts to use the Crown lands at low rents.

It is a mini-wildlife agency, with powers superior in some ways to the provincial agency. It could serve as a model for wildlife development on specific areas but it seems highly improbable that resource legislation concerned with forage, forests and land would allow the same authority over extensive areas of wildlife habitat.

Between 1966 and the next act consolidation in 1982, there was constant updating of the existing Act. New problems and opportunities arose and tested the scope of the enabling legislation. Amendments were required each year and, gradually, the Act took on the characteristic patchwork appearance of all such legislation, prior to major revisions. In 1969 the new guiding regulations were passed but it was not until 1971 that the first certificate was granted. It is worth noting that, from the first serious discussion in 1964, the enabling legislation in 1966, specific regulations in 1969, and actual implementation in 1971, some seven years had elapsed. This major change was brought in, step by step, through consultation and negotiation. While it seems an overly long time, it may represent a practical time-frame to effect major changes when altering the basics of an industry, protecting individual guides, and ensuring the rights of residents to use wildlife.

In 1971 the humane trapping movement became a new and potent factor in fur management. It was one of the first groups concerned with cruelty to animals and this concern grew rapidly into broad support for the rights of animals. The Wildlife Branch recognized the validity of some of those concerns and joined Ontario, Manitoba, Saskatchewan, the Canadian Association for Humane Trapping and the Society for Prevention of Cruelty to Animals to supply money for studies at several universities, to find effective and humane replacements for the leg-hold trap. From this beginning, and over the next 15 years, changes in trapping systems were introduced to make trapping more humane. Regulations were brought in nearly every year on such subjects as trapper education, trapper licencing requirements, abolishing certain trap usages, requirements for trap inspections and modifications to existing traps. The anti-trapping campaign radically altered the wild fur industry and caused the agency to participate in a nation-wide program to make trapping more humane, culminating in 1983 in the Fur Institute of Canada. These ideas started the change in the public's and the agency's perception of what is acceptable use of the wildlife resource. The impact of these thoughts continues.

Specific new management regulations were continually being imposed. Helicopters were banned from transporting hunters or game, in a successful attempt to control access to game herds by use of this unsporting technology.

By 1974, however, it was obvious that short seasons, vehicle limitations, ability to swiftly close seasons, etc. were not always capable of limiting game harvests to predictable results. The answer was Limited Entry Hunts. This process, through a random selection of applicants, limits the number of hunters so that a predetermined kill may be achieved for a species or sex in a given area. It limits the harvest and maintains the quality of the hunting experience. It will play an increasing role in future intensive management strategy.

The trend to value the hunting experience rather than the animal was reinforced when the trophy system was replaced in 1974 with a species licence system for non-residents. The new system substituted a much higher tag licence fee as the charge for an opportunity to hunt. There were no further charges if successful and no rebate if unsuccessful. It also eliminated evasion of the trophy fee.

The need for more specific information about some species than is provided by questionnaires resulted in compulsory inspection regulations in 1978. All caribou, mountain goat, mountain sheep and grizzly bear had to be presented for inspection within a stated period after the hunt. The data gathered have been invaluable in assessing strategy so that improvements could be made. Compulsory inspection continues and expands.

A significant new source of revenue was found in 1980 with the establishment of the Habitat Conservation Fund. It is based on a surcharge of $3 on every primary hunting, fishing, trapping and guiding licence issued. The income goes into a special non-lapsing account, not into general revenue. These funds are to be used to acquire land, improve and enhance habitat, advance knowledge about the fish and wildlife resources, re-introduce species to former ranges, etc., but it must not be used for permanent salaries or routine costs. An advisory committee recommends to the Minister a priorized list of projects suggested by the agency and the public. Approximately $1.5 million is raised annually and provides the funds for 40 to 50 projects, which can be implemented by the agency or contracted out.

The current Wildlife Act passed by the legislature in 1982 was preceeded by a discussion paper to promote review and comment. It stressed interpretation by defining many new terms so that the legislation would be better understood. It defined ownership of wildlife, outlined steps to manage wildlife, proposed non-profit and commercial ways to use wildlife, and emphasized ways and means to maintain, protect and enhance wildlife habitat. Strong legislation was proposed on all of those topics and many others based on the two principal goals for wildlife:

54

1. To maintain the diversity of species representative of the major biophysical zones of the province, and

2. To ensure that, within the constraints of land capability and the biological limits of each species, wildlife is available in sufficient abundance to meet the social, recreational, ecological and economic needs of society.

These goals served as the unoffical preamble to the new act. And, for the first time since the Preservation of the Game Act of 1859, the content of the proposed legislation could be judged by stated standards, a practice that deserves support.

The Act in its final form failed to meet all the needs outlined in the discussion paper but there were many significant advances. The major deficiency was in the habitat section, where authority to maintain or enhance key wildlife habitat on Crown land was not approved. To date, wildlife habitat does not receive legal protection except on land under Ministry control. There is no requirement for other resource agencies to enter into co-operative agreements to benefit wildlife, nor is there enough effective pressure to bring about a resource co-ordination act. Resource acts all too often are administered in a unilateral manner due, mainly, to their bottom line requirement.

The act of 1982 did, however, provide much needed enabling sections for more intensive management, substantially raised penalties including mandatory licence cancellation for the more serious crimes, clearly defined the powers of the Minister, Director and Regional Managers, emphasized that wildlife belongs to the Crown and set forth its right to animals that escape and the liability of the person responsible. Critical areas or sanctuaries can be created to protect threatened or endangered species but only in a Wildlife Management Area which is land under the administration of the Minster and where the Wildlife Act takes precedence.

Regional managers became responsible for commercial licences, permits and guide quotas. The definition section was increased to include keywords such as animal, critical wildlife area, domestic animal, endangered species, wildlife habitat, quota and wildlife.

Probably the most significant initiative was the provision for the Minister to enter into agreements with anybody for the purpose of improving the wildlife resource and its use. As governments draw back from increased expenditure and more staff, the opportunity grows for a larger role for the private sector, ranging from non-profit arrangements to commercial ventures. This section could provide one way for the private sector to be involved. Naturalists, game clubs, forest companies, and Indian Bands are some of the private sector groups which could negotiate agreements to benefit wildlife and themselves, hopefully with the provision that any partnership recognizes that wildlife still belongs to the Crown.

Overall, the Wildlife Act of 1982 was an improved instrument upon which to base management of the Wildlife resource. It is equally true that amendments to update the act will continue. It is an evolutionary process driven by society's perceptions and understanding about old problems and new issues. The Indian situation, private development of wildlife for profit and non-profit purposes, integration of wildlife habitat with the needs of other renewable resources, improved enforcement based on public support, a more informed public on predation and animal rights, and the need for wildlife to enter more fully into our economic culture are a few of the issues that will provide substance for debate leading to future act amendments. This evolution of wildlife legislation quite likely will continue to establish conditional rights for some people to manage and use wildlife. The common property resource use pattern established in 1859 will gradually erode in response to society's changing values, similar to the erosion of the monopolistic tenures of aboriginal people in response to western values.

"The Laws of God, the laws of man,
He may keep that will and can;
Not I: let God and man decree
Laws for themselves and not for me."

A. E. Housman
Last Poems

Making the law is one thing; enforcing it is quite another. The judicial
system — legislatures and the courts — have given wildlife laws lower
priority than regular criminal law. An extra duck in the bag was
regarded, and probably properly so, as less significant than robbing a
store. But isn't shooting an extra duck the same kind of thing as
stealing a loaf of bread or a throw-away cigarette lighter. In one case
the loser is the store owner; it's easy to quantify his loss. In the other
case, the loser is society; who really suffers that loss? Everybody's child
is nobody's child. Or so it seems.

The story of enforcement in British Columbia is a mixed bag of
enthusiasm and disregard, of commitment and dismissal. For a long
time, however, the enforcement arm of the various ministries that
looked after wildlife was sadly neglected and understaffed. In recent
years, that has changed a bit but the demands on the wildlife
enforcement officer have not. New technology has helped the law but
it has also helped the violator — better access, better vehicles, better
equipment, better radios. It is still a matter of an officer going into the
woods alone to find and face down one or several armed men who
may be commiting a serious offence. As Gilbert and Sullivan once
said, "A policeman's lot is not a happy one."

The consequences of illegal hunting have not been adequately
documented, but knowledgeable field people are convinced, and
convincing, that it poses a serious danger for some species of wildlife.
It is ironic that legitimate hunters must put up with reduced hunting
seasons and bag limits because their quarry is being taken by poachers
and other criminals.

CHAPTER 4

The Law and the Poacher

David J. Spalding

The laws came first. Before there were game laws in British Columbia there was no poaching and there were no poachers. With the coming of laws there came also the need to develop a special body of lawmen to uphold those laws. For many years those officers were known as Game Wardens. In 1958 they took the new name of Conservation Officer, a title which reflected their new responsibilities. Since the creation of the first game warden, a war has waged between lawmen and poachers: a war that is sometimes carried on with good humour, sometimes with deadly intent, but always in earnest.

There is good reason for the earnest pursuit of game laws. Too often we forget that those animals we want nearby are, in human terms, silent. They cannot call out in their extremity, "Enough." The wildlife laws, designed and enforced by both biologists and conservation officers, are the first (and often the only) line of defence for that great, silent multitude which share the land with us.

There is an impressive, and intimidating, collection of statistics dealing with wildlife enforcement in British Columbia. I will not deal with these in this chapter, but I will begin with two sets of numbers. Bryan Williams' appointment in 1905 provided British Columbia with its first Provincial Game and Forest Warden. I do not know how many poachers there were in 1905, but there were 23 convictions relating to wildlife offences. Eighty years later (1985) there were 99 enforcement officers in the field and 3,424 charges laid. Clearly, there are many people who are caught breaking British Columbia's wildlife laws and it is safe to assume there are many who break the law and are never caught.

The Poacher

At the outset, I would like to set the tone of this chapter. Catching poachers is rarely easy and it is often dangerous. Poachers, by definition, have broken the law and as law-breakers they present a potential danger to the investigating officer. Some poachers verbally abuse the officer, some threaten physical harm or death and some must be physically restrained. Quite recently an officer was struck on the head with a rifle. Another was beaten. In one instance an officer was shot and wounded. In two others, officers have been killed while on duty.

Two types of investigation pose special problems: undercover work and night patrols. The undercover officer is under constant pressure to maintain the image of a criminal willingly working with criminals. Officers on night patrol are working in isolated areas, never knowing what or who they are going to encounter. Because I have accompanied officers on night patrols (not many, I must admit) I have experienced at least some of the questions which must be dealt with: who is in the next vehicle and what have they been doing, will they be armed, will they have game, are they desperate enough to run, are they desperate enough to shoot?

Catching poachers is not only a necessary business, it is a dangerous business.

I have divided the reasons for poaching into four categories: need, ignorance, profit and culture. Underlying each of these sometimes is the element of challenge: to break a law and get away with it, to challenge authority. More often than not there is the philosophy described in my opening quote: let the law apply to others, not to me.

Need

During the early history of this province, when it was truly a frontier, there was a need by settlers, miners, trappers and explorers to take game year-round, and it was the accepted thing to do. My grandfather (an early settler) kept a diary for many years and recorded an astounding number of deer killed each year to keep his family in meat. For many of the early settlers, money was scarce, stores distant and game abundant.

Trappers and prospectors were in the field for months at a time and lived under conditions where hunting was the only alternative to starvation.

When I first joined the Wildlife Branch in the early 1960's, it was still common for guides to refer to "camp meat." This referred to the practice of shooting the first available ungulate to provide meat for guides and hunters alike at the start of a hunt. Camp meat was considered an extra and not worth recording as a kill. This practice undoubtedly began as a need and then continued as a considered right for many years.

As the province developed, as the need to conserve wildlife gained acceptance and as social services increased, the argument of "need" to take game out of season lost its earlier justification. Nowadays, although some may still claim it, need is only rarely recognized as legitimate.

Ignorance

Those who take game illegally, but in ignorance of the law, are not poaching. However, their actions have the same effect as those of the poacher: an animal is lost that should not have been lost. Fortunately, those who are truly ignorant of the laws or the animals they pursue are in a minority.

New Canadians sometimes find their ignorance of our laws leads to trouble. Some coming from a background where small birds are considered to be a good source of protein, regarded starlings in the Okanagan orchards as fair game. In fact, because starlings are pests, we encouraged the shooting, trapping and snaring of those birds. However, as time went on, Branch staff received reports that meadowlarks and red-winged blackbirds were also ending up in meat-pies. It was then that our laws had to be explained in some detail to our newer citizens.

Mandatory hunter training programs, a greater awareness of wildlife values and a growing need for conservation are all slowly reducing the number of hunters who take game in ignorance of the law.

Profit

There is money to be made from wildlife. On the one hand, trapping and guiding are two legitimate methods of turning a profit, or at least of making a living. On the other hand, poachers have taken, and probably will continue to take, great risks to achieve financial gain from the sale of a fascinating variety of animals and animal parts.

The most common saleable item is meat. An example from the 1950's illustrates this and also shows that sometimes an investigation can be quite easy. An officer, not in uniform, overheard a man in a coffee shop tell another that he would soon have money as he had some moose meat for sale. As the prospective vendor left the restaurant, the officer followed him outside and indicated he would like to buy some moose meat. Following some negotiating and a trip to view the moose, a sale price of $200 for two moose carcasses was arranged. During the negotiations, the officer discovered that the poacher had already sold about 25 deer carcasses. The officer paid the money, then identified himself as a game warden and escorted the culprit off to jail. The culprit was later tried and convicted.

A successful investigation was concluded recently in the Prince George area. Following a tip, the enforcement staff investigated suspicions that moose meat was being sold, disguised as sausage. This was found to be true. The shop was raided and about 11,000 pounds of meat were seized. Biologists determined that 9,000 pounds of it was moose meat. They also determined that about 37 average-size moose were required to obtain that quantity of meat. The butcher was charged, convicted and fined $3,800 and lost his equipment. That is very likely the largest quantity of game meat ever seized in British Columbia.

Undercover officers are increasingly used, and to good advantage. The cost is high but the rewards can be great. One successful example from Vancouver Island is worth relating. In the early 1980's, the enforcement staff in Nanaimo heard rumours of deer and elk poaching, and game meat being sold to restaurants. Two undercover officers were sent into the area of suspected poaching, disguised as shake-bolt-cutters. They gained the confidence of three suspects. The subsequent investigation took two months of intensive undercover work. The officers accompanied the poachers on three pit-lamping hunts, bought deer from them and finally gathered enough information to lay charges. All three suspects were convicted and received jail terms of two to four months.

Unfortunately, such investigations are not always quite so easy or so successful. Once, in Smithers, we received several reports that moose meat was being sold in Lower Post, a small community near the British Columbia-Yukon boundary. We arranged to have an undercover officer go into the community and see what he could find. He picked up scraps of hearsay evidence but nothing concrete. After a week of frustration, he had to leave, empty-handed.

Another area where poachers are encouraged by high returns is the sale of trophy heads and capes. There are some hunters, fortunately a minority, who receive more enjoyment from displaying a large head on their wall than from the satisfaction gained in the knowledge that their trophy was taken in fair chase. Such men will pay several thousand dollars for a remarkable head, no matter how it is taken. A celebrated case, involving trophy rams and non-residents, took place in the Kootenays in the early 1980's. A conservation officer became suspicious when a guide consistently reported that his hunters were taking large rams. These suspicions led to a lengthy investigation involving British Columbia, Parks Canada and United States officials. After two years it was established that the guide was guiding hunters outside his territory and often in Banff and Jasper National Parks. There was some evidence to suggest the guide photographed large rams in Banff and then found prospective hunters (who were well aware they were about to hunt in a park) on the basis of the photographs. The guide was convicted on three counts of guiding illegally, fined $4,000, jailed for 75 days, and lost his guide territory. One American hunter was prosecuted by United States officials, fined $12,000 and jailed.

More unusual, yet saleable, items are: gallbadders and claws from bears (used as aphrodisiacs), elk teeth, deer hoofs, eagle feathers and goat horns.

Finally, special mention must be made of falcons. Falcons are beautiful birds. They arc great hunters and in high demand by falconers. I have been unable to establish a firm price, but rumoured prices vary from $2,000 to $25,000 per bird.

The falcon poacher does not have an easy time of it, especially on the coast, as there are many problems which must be overcome before the birds or eggs are safe at home. A boat, plane or helicopter must be arranged to transport the group and its equipment to the general vicinity of the nest site. The nests, located on steep cliffs, must be found. Difficult descents and ascents must be made (climbing gear and ropes are generally needed) and the climb back with either chicks or eggs is particularly critical. All this time, the poacher must be alert for conservation officers, inquisitive residents or curious boaters. In addition, suspicions of the charter boat skipper or the pilot must be allayed. Even when the poacher, in the case of a Queen Charlotte Islands operation, returns with his bounty to one of the communities on the Islands, he is not out of the woods. Motel and hotel operators are on the alert for falcon theft, so continued caution is required. Eggs must be incubated, chicks must be fed. And then there is the long trip home, whether to somewhere in British Columbia, the United States or Europe. Perhaps these challenges are part of the falcon poacher's incentive.

Falcon poaching takes place throughout the province but most activity is centred on the Queen Charlotte Islands (and to a lesser extent on the Scott Islands). When I was stationed in Smithers, we initiated an intensive falcon patrol during the spring of each year in an attempt to eliminate the taking of young birds or eggs or both from the nest. Fortunately, for the Branch and the falcons, Queen Charlotte Island residents are very protective of "their" falcons. We received both encouragement and assistance from charter boat owners, pilots and many others. A good example of this is an investigation which took place about four years ago.

Two non-residents chartered a helicopter on the Charlottes, flew out to Langara Island and collected one young peregrine. The helicopter pilot was alerted that something might be wrong as they acted suspiciously when he picked them up. He reported his suspicions to the conservation officer in Queen Charlotte City who, with a federal fisheries officer as back-up, went to the hotel where the two suspects were staying. After some negotiating, they gained entry to the room. They first noticed a rifle and, following some questioning, determined the suspects had no firearms permit. This gave them the authority to search the room and they quickly located a young falcon in the bathroom. A scuffle followed, one man was subdued but the second suspect escaped with the bird. He was chased and finally captured. During the chase the suspect discarded the falcon which was later found dead. Both suspects were jailed, taken to court and fined $1,000 each.

We were not always successful. Several years ago a party of non-residents chartered a boat on the Charlottes and went out to Langara Island, ostensibly on a photographic safari. It was discovered later that this story was a hoax and the real purpose was to collect falcon eggs. Either five or six eggs were taken from nests and placed inside down-filled pockets in the poacher's vests which kept the eggs warm until the men could get them back to a portable incubator. They remained in the incubator until the party returned to Europe. It was only later that the boat owner decided that something might have been wrong and he then reported to the conservation officer. Subsequent investigation disclosed the full story, but too late to lay charges.

Tradition and Culture

This chapter, or this book, is not the place to deal with the issue of Indian versus non-Indian or the relative supremacy of federal/provincial law or Indian tradition. However, in terms of provincial law, Indians sometimes take wildlife illegally. Not only are the animals taken illegally, but the taking of deer and moose in the winter for food, the taking of goats for their hides for ceremonial blankets and the taking of eagles for feathers can and does threaten the survival of some wildlife populations. In many areas of the interior, Indians live and hunt on land used as winter range by deer and moose. Out-of-season hunting plays havoc with the management programs of the biologists and can negate much of their effort.

But it is not a simple matter. The men enforcing provincial game laws have no alternative: the laws apply to all equally. Indian demands are rooted in a long tradition of use which often conflicts with non-Indian management plans. The battle continues, in and out of the courts, and I only hope that, when the second centennial wildlife book appears, the author who repeats this chapter will be able to say to his readers, "Thank God, we solved that one."

The Courts

When a suspected violation has been investigated and the suspected violator(s) found and charged, the entire process is, by and large, over for the field officer: the matter passes to the courts. Control is out of the hands of the investigating officer. Although that is right, and fair, the fact that adjudication is decided in a new arena leads to repeated frustration. We often hear the complaint that "The prosecutor let us down," or "The Judge was far too lenient," or "We lost on a technicality." This last is a miserable business and I have sympathized with several officers, during my years in the Branch, who had worked very hard over days, weeks or months of investigation, only to have a deserved conviction for a serious infraction dismissed for some minor procedural mistake. One of the great advantages of the present concentration on enforcement by the new Conservation Officer Service is that charges are, generally speaking, laid with much more attention to both technical and legal detail.

Concern about the judicial process is certainly not new. From the beginning, Bryan Williams frequently complained of leniency in the court. Yet, reviewing the record, one can only wonder. To pick a few examples may not be fair but the severity of these instances must have acted as a forceful reminder to the would-be poacher: 1906 — one month in jail for having in possession one cow elk; 1915 — $1,000 fine for shooting a cow caribou; 1918 — two months in jail for killing grouse during closed season; 30 days in jail for pit-lamping; 1919 — 60 days in jail for pit-lamping. The severity of those judgements is not typical but it was not unusual in those early days for poachers to receive jail sentences, quite substantial fines, or both.

An example from the 1950's shows that the courts continued (perhaps not always consistently) to remain sensitive to wildlife issues. A non-resident flew into the Cariboo District from the United States, shot a bighorn ram during a closed season and flew out with the carcass. He very nearly got away with it but an alert border official noticed the carcass and an investigation was initiated by both British Columbian and American officials. The poacher was apprehended, his plane was seized, he was fined $1,000 and he lost his trophy.

Very recently in the Peace River area a non-resident, masquerading as a resident, was fined $1,800 for shooting a bear. There is an interesting sequel to this story. The convicted hunter, who does reside part-time in the province, paid his fine and later contributed an additional $500 to wildlife conservation. Five men on Vancouver Island were fined a total of $4,600 for shooting two elk out of season. Their rifles were confiscated, their hunting licences cancelled for five years and their vehicle seized and held for a considerable time before released.

To further assist the courts, the Wildlife Act now contains provisions for fines of up to $10,000 and a six-month jail term — potentially, very strong deterrents.

I have not highlighted these noteworthy penalties with the intent of misleading readers into complacency. Judgements are sometimes difficult to understand. An example from the north illustrates this:

In the late 1970's, an alert licence vendor reported to his conservation officer that a non-resident had requested a hunting licence, yet had no guide. Non-residents can hunt only if they are accompanied by a licenced game guide. Nor did the visitor know where he was going to hunt. An investigation was initiated and an electronic bug was placed on the suspect's vehicle. The officers suspected he was shooting bear and they knew he was buying furs illegally. After some days of trailing the suspect, aided by the electronic bug, the officers stopped him on a back road and found several illegal furs in his truck. He was apprehended, taken to court, found guilty and fined $900. So far, so good, but he was allowed to keep one-half of the furs, furs which were illegally in his possession and, therefore, not legally his.

Such judgements leave the impression that at least some judges do not care very much about wildlife.

Conservation Officer Service

This last part of my contribution to our centennial celebration is both the easiest and the most difficult to discuss: the easiest because I am, to a large extent, dealing with the heroes of my story, yet difficult because the conservation officer's position, his responsibilities and his view of his role often lead to unhappiness and discord.

I have taken some time to develop a theme of conflict, despite the many splendid times I have spent (and every other field biologist has spent, and is spending) with conservation officers, on wildlife surveys, game counts, game checks, habitat improvement programs, enforcement patrols, hunting and fishing trips and social occasions. The good times and the co-operative, productive programs are very real. Yet, too often, underlying tensions have been there, stated or unstated. This issue has been an integral part of British Columbia's management program for many years, so, although we have every right to celebrate, it does no harm to recognize that the years of progress have not always been "easy, easy, all the way."

In the beginning there were the game wardens: men whose interests and capabilities led them to an outdoor life, to a frontier life where formal education was not an issue. They participated in the moulding and enforcement of laws designed to protect the fish and wildlife they loved. They were more than policemen. They felt it their responsibility to know as much as possible about the wildlife and fish within their districts. Many were keen naturalists, some were excellent photographers and most hunted and fished. They were in the field most of the time and took pride in knowing the geography of the areas where they worked. The Chief Game Warden's reports, and later the Game Commission reports, included fascinating accounts from the different wardens: the pressure of hunting and poaching, the effects of weather, the condition of animals, the state of different populations, the recommendations to maintain or improve the populations.

The power to protect and manage the resource was in the hands of the game wardens. The individual officer received respect and support from headquarters, his recommendations were listened to and he was admired in his community. He was regarded as both a policeman and an expert on most outdoor matters.

By the early 1950's, the new science of wildlife management, developing to a large extent at the universities and practiced by young men and women graduates, was gaining respect for its contributions to wildlife conservation. In 1947 the first biologist came on the Game Commission staff. There is nothing in the records to suggest any dissenting voice over this move. In fact, there was frequent and glowing praise for the help provided by the new science.

During these early years there were few biologists and their slowly accumulating data were limited. They were the experts and their time was coming, but each game warden (soon to be called conservation officer) was still "Mr. Fish and Wildlife" in his district. A January, 1956, article in the *Wildlife Review*, entitled "What Does a Game Warden Do?" summarizes it well: he is on duty 24 hours a day, licences and supervises guides and trappers, issues a variety of licences, enforces all hunting and fishing regulations, conducts checks on hunters and fishermen, carries out some predator control and some nuisance animal control, acts as game management agent in his district (this would include participating in game and fish surveys, and conducting routine winter and spring counts), records changing wildlife conditions (including furbearers), assists with fish and pheasant liberations, patrols game reserves, speaks to a variety of public groups, acts as public relations man for the Branch in his district, sometimes organizes junior wildlife clubs, checks and reports on water pollution problems, checks and reports on applications for water use, maintains office work and, when he gets a chance, reads up on the latest trends in wildlife management.

Truly, the game warden was expected to be all things to all people. And many of them managed to pull it off. I have been to retirement parties for such men whose long careers had ended. The admiration and respect of their fellow workers, and the community members who had watched them work, was impressive to behold and hear.

However, the voices of the early biologists began to be heard. They, too, were strong, outspoken men who knew that, in the long run, their new science was the only way both to use and to protect the province's wildlife. Their ideas of seasons, bag-limits, any-sex harvests, openings, closings and the imperative of habitat seemed, at the time, revolutionary. Their recommendations were only slowly, and sometimes reluctantly, accepted. Increasingly, the relative merits of the book-learning of the biologists versus the experience of the conservation officers were debated topics.

The tone and direction of wildlife management and administration in this province, have, by and large, been set by the organization's leaders. This position has had several titles: Provincial Game and Forest Warden at first, then Game Commissioner(s) and finally Director. Until 1962, this position had always been held by a man with a strong game warden background. In 1963, the Director's position was filled by a biologist and it became clear to all that the power had finally shifted from the game warden/conservation officer group to the biologists.

I am not implying there was anything sinister in this. There was no Machiavellian plot by the biologists to do in the conservation officers. The pre-emptive decision taken in 1947 to hire the first biologist could have led to no other outcome. The demands and complexity of the resource required managers and administrators with a high level of sophisticated training.

There was no plot but I now wonder if we (I joined the Branch in 1963) fully realized the impact this shift of power was having on the conservation officers. They came to realize they had less authority and stature, yet were expected to carry out new and sometimes unwanted responsibilities — the responsibilities of wildlife, fisheries and habitat protection technicians, under the direction of well-educated but often otherwise inexperienced biologists.

We biologists did not always assist in the smooth transition of power. We were proud of our knowledge and sometimes flaunted it. We challenged the conservation officer's "layman's" knowledge. We occasionally provoked them by deriding their enforcement efforts. We sometimes asserted our new role without due regard for the sensibilities, the professional integrity and achievements of the field officers.

I can highlight this with an example from my own experience which I hope is not typical, but which, by its extremity, illustrates the problem. As Regional Director in Smithers I was faced with a very real problem of organizing a large trapline file. Part of this included the preparation of maps showing the boundaries of each line. We were short of staff so I insisted our senior conservation officer (the man who was second-in-command of the regional enforcement program!) prepare the maps. I am appalled now at the insensitivity of this decision and, when I recently reminded that officer of the trapline map issue, we both laughed, ruefully. I agreed I would not make such a demand now. I also admitted I would never have ordered a biologist to carry out such work.

At a more significant level, we biologists rubbed salt into the wounds of the conservation officers: educational requirements of senior field positions and most senior headquarters positions effectively removed conservation officers from competition.

The years of "togetherness" were not always easy and many conservation officers experienced frustration and anger, emotions that were not always contained. The officers, on occasion, were quick to remind biologists of their management mistakes; they sometimes were unable to show up for assigned management duties; there were times, admittedly infrequent, when officers supported the public in the latter's condemnations of new management procedures. One example (and again I have resorted to an extreme) focuses attention on the deepening rift developing between the biologists and the conservation officers.

In late 1977, a judicial inquiry was initiated to investigate some branch procedures and the activities of some branch staff. Three of the four staff named in the inquiry were biologists. (I was one of them.) I must stress that the conservation officer/biologist rift was not the reason for the inquiry. The inquiry had been called following an enforcement investigation of a guide-outfitter which, in turn, led to a disclosure of questionable practices in the issuing of several documents relating to the guide-outfitter. What I found unusual at the time was the extraordinary enthusiasm with which the early investigation, carried out by conservation officers, proceeded.

This very uneasy relationship between biologist and conservation officer was noted by Inquiry Commissioner McCarthy: "The evidence has revealed a substantial gap to exist between the biologist and enforcement elements within the Branch. There appear to be deep-rooted differences between these two elements and resentment has naturally been a by-product of this division." (McCarthy, J.L., Commissioner, Interim Report. Ministry of Recreation and Conservation, Victoria, B.C. 1978. p. 89.) In hindsight, and if my thesis supporting the role of power (and the gain or loss thereof) is accepted, it was an understandable response to years of frustration.

One of life's few predictables is change and, in 1980, change came for the conservation officers. A new and expanding Ministry of Environment required greater enforcement capability. To achieve it, a new and separate Conservation Officer Service was created. This new Service was welcomed by the majority of conservation officers. As it now stands (1987) the Service supplies investigative and enforcement capabilities for five Ministry branches: wildlife, fisheries, waste management, water management and pesticide control.

When the Ministry assigned these expanded responsibilities to the new service they were aware there would inevitably be a loss of some old responsibilities. There was a cost involved. Depending upon whom I have spoken to, the cost has been either greater or lesser, but can be summarized as follows:

1. A loss of contact between the public and the district conservation officer. It was reassuring for many hunters, fishermen and others, to visit their district office and discuss a variety of fish and/or wildlife issues, only some of which were related to enforcement. Additionally, this public contact provided both an opportunity for the district officer to explain management programs and a chance to relay public impressions back to the biologist.

2. A disappointment for some conservation officers whose interests lay not only in enforcement but also with many of the technical aspects of wildlife (and fisheries) management.

3. A loss of good technical assistance for several management programs.

4. There is a fear from some that the new service will bend all its efforts to prosecutions and convictions, with emphasis on quantity.

Only time will show the full impact of the present separation of enforcement from management. But it is my belief that the change has been for the better. The very real costs are out-weighed by the benefits. My research for this chapter has not been exhaustive but the officers I spoke to seem, generally, happier than they used to be, pleased with their new service, enthusiastic about their investigations. One officer, who was opposed to the change when it began, now sees the growing need for more enforcement. They have just begun to scratch the surface. Others mention the benefit of increased training in procedures, better preparation for court, an opportunity to spend time (sometimes a loss of time and money) to solve difficult investigations.

I have been told repeatedly by conservation officers and some regional managers that contact and co-operation can, and does, take place between management and enforcement. I have one final anecdote to illustrate this. A wildlife biologist was hunting chukar partridge near Kamloops Lake when his dog found a wild sheep carcass, recently killed and with the head removed. Hoof measurements established the carcass to be that of an adult ram. The biologist reported his findings to the enforcement service as the carcass was located in an area closed to sheep hunting. Little was heard for about a year and then word came back that a conservation officer had seized a ram head which the officer felt may have been killed illegally in the area where the sheep carcass had been found. The biologist retrieved the skeletal remains and turned them over to the conservation officer who, with the aid of outside experts, was able to determine there was a very strong likelihood the seized head belonged to the headless skeleton. This case has not been concluded and, for the sake of my argument, the outcome does not matter. What does matter is the real concern, expressed by both biologist and conservation officer, to poaching.

". . . I believe a chance to see wildlife under natural conditions is one of the important rights of man. It is a real enrichment of living. Believing this, I often feel that the right to hunt and kill game is far more questionable than the right simply to see it and watch it for the pleasure of seeing and watching, and perhaps learning a little. But my conviction on this point is far out weighed by the realization that hunters are almost the only effective protection of wildlife."

Roderick Haig-Brown
Writings and Reflections

Few places in North American offer as much variety and opportunity for hunters, variety of species and of terrain, and opportunity to hunt alone or with guides. The hunting season for one animal or another extends for months. Costs are high but generally not prohibitive. Access is increasingly easier. Animal numbers, for most species and in most places, but not all, are generally good. In short, British Columbia is a good place for the recreational hunter.

Some would that this were not so. They argue strenuously that hunting should be prohibited as a sign that man is becoming more civilized. Others argue, with equal vigour, that hunting is a part of man's nature and that to deny him the right to hunt is to truncate his genetic birthright. The animal is presumably indifferent to both arguments. It lives constantly on the edge, every day is a challenge to its survival.

While a good many hunters feel a oneness with the animal they pursue and treat it with respect, many others, perhaps the majority, have lost something of the tradition of hunting and the ethics of the chase. Smearing blood on a young hunter from his first kill may not appeal to all of us but at least it symbolized that the animal was more than just meat.

The chase was once a more equal match than it is today. Modern equipment seems to give the hunter an edge although success rates belie that suggestion. Good game management will ensure that modern technology is not used to the detriment of the species.

Hunters more than any group have struggled to maintain high animal numbers in the face of mounting pressure on the resource. For many, the commitment is made not with an eye to next winter's larder but simply with a love for wildlife.

CHAPTER 5

The Hunting Tradition

Mike Halleran

This chapter is a blend of two writings by the same author, but prepared across a wide interval of both distance and time. One part is from an earlier essay on the hunting tradition first published in the *Vancouver Sun* about ten years ago. It was written on a stormy fall afternoon in the author's home in an isolated part of the West Kootenay district. The rest of the chapter was written in the spring of 1987 in a Vancouver highrise hotel.

The contrast in these two settings is characteristic of the diversity of lifestyles and locations typical of modern British Columbia. On one hand, a beautiful, modern and international city. On the other, an island of human habitation amid a sea of largely unoccupied mountains. There are staunch defenders of wildlife in both kinds of setting and all manner of places between. But today, many of those who love and defend wildlife are opposed to a continuation of the hunting tradition.

There are also tens of thousands of British Columbia residents who go hunting each year. Just as there is great diversity in British Columbia's environments and lifestyles, so there is much divergence on the relevance of hunting. It is not the lack of sameness but our failure to accept it, that is the source of so much conflict and social agony.

"Man the hunter" is a figure whose movements can be backtracked through the dusts of time. Modern, present day hunting traditions derive from that experience and it is my contention that, like most modern hunters, our prehistoric ancestor hunted for pleasure as well as protein. And, of course, the hunter presence has prevailed for a very long time. Man hunted for millions of years but came to question that activity only within the last century. If the longer span of time were represented by a kilometre of distance, the period in which it has been called to question would be only a centimetre or two.

Somewhere along the way, a kind of warm-blood bias began to emerge. It is interesting to consider why people instinctively feel bound to resist cruelty to "animals" but may be quite unconcerned about inflicting pain on fish, reptiles or amphibians. These peculiarities cannot be explained by the purely physiological differences among the species, particularly insofar as their response to pain is concerned. I was once informed that the lateral line of salmonids has a pain sensitivity about equal to the cornea of the human eye. That may explain why, as one takes a small trout in hand to disgorge the hook, there are some very violent contortions on the part of the animal. But being voiceless, the fish can make no audible expression of its pain. One is inclined to believe that if it could cry out, angling might be a much less popular pastime.

The glaring inconsistency in our traditional approaches to these matters would be hard to explain to a visitor from another planet. How could we justify our treatment of various animals with varying degrees of either kindness or cruelty, a part of our behaviour not only lacking in scientific awareness but defying logic as well.

We would never think of "angling" for mallards or Canada geese yet, no doubt, one could likely find a bait on which to catch them. It would certainly inflict enormous pain but it is seen as perfectly acceptable to afford such treatment to fish. It is one of those human contradictions that cannot be explained in rational terms. In present day perceptions of wildlife, such contradictions abound. Across the ages we have come to treat fish differently than warm-blooded animals, not because they are so different, but because the warm-bloods are more like us.

The timeless exposure of humans to hunting has resulted in some social extensions of the tradition that go far beyond the hunt itself. The respect, fear, even reverence which hunting societies came to hold for wildlife is visible in early art forms (some of which still survive) and, later, in traditions of heraldry and dress. Many of these predate religion, language and politics. Such traditions even continue to evolve as society finds more and more ways by which to "possess" wildlife, even profit from them. We put their images on our coins and name football teams after them — even cars — which I suppose, must be the ultimate urban compliment. The trend to commercialization is reaching new heights with the moves to confine wild animals on "farms" and/or "ranches" so as to increase profit potential by selling hunting privileges, meat and certain body parts for aphrodisiacs and similar purposes.

There seems to be a sufficient number of domestic species without setting out to domesticate still more.

Gross examples of commercial exploitation can also be found in television and the film industry, which have manufactured (and successfully marketed) several generations of wildlife cartoon characters, some of whom walk upright, converse among species and even pick up things with their "hands." The whole process is rife with anthropomorphism and leaves some sadly distorted impressions with the watcher — especially with the young.

Just as the tradition of hunting is itself timeless, so is the tradition of patriarchs or older family members introducing children to the hunt. Such is the experience of both my wife's family and my own. The hunting tradition is also a hallmark of British Columbia's own special kind of land classification, which sees over ninety percent of the land base still vested in public ownership. When the land and its wildlife remain part of the commons it is easier to maintain environmental values in some kind of equitable viability. So, in the western nations (and especially in the western parts of this nation), the hunting tradition is a creature of public ownership of land as well as a protector of it.

Even at that, most of the hunting I do is on my own land. The meadows around our valley-bottom home have provided a mainstay of family meat for five generations. This must qualify as a "hunting tradition." It exists in many similar parts of the province and I would like to see it continue. Although I much prefer wild meat to tame, and greatly enjoy the autumn ritual of hunting, I do not hunt only for the meat. I have other reasons for going.

The natural history of these meadows is fascinating. Understanding something about the wildlife habitat in which one hunts (and lives) is part of the hunting tradition as well. These are natural meadows, never treed. Deciduous thickets abound but much of our place is open grassland — actually, old lake bottom. The meadows flood sometimes, another reason why they were never forested. We have seen whitecaps on those meadows. Over most of the year they are excellent habitat for whitetail deer. And at various times we see waterfowl, elk, raptors, even grizzly bear. But most of these sightings are less frequent in the fall. The deer and elk make themselves scarce during the hunting season. Do you suppose they know?

I cannot write authoritatively about the hunting traditions of other families but those of my own extended family are, of course, well known to me. My wife's grandfather first hunted here in 1912. Wild meat was even more a mainstay in those days and such was largely free for the taking. One observes the game laws today but in the life of this valley, game laws are relatively new. If they existed in 1912, there was no enforcement of them. People shot what they needed and that was that. If overhunting did occur it was not of serious consequence, since populations have continued to remain viable despite a century of hunting.

Much pioneer income came from trapping, another aspect of the hunting tradition. I encourage others to trap my land but do no trapping myself. This is not a biased value judgement, merely a matter of personal choice. I hope it is not a sign of the times. Have I allowed the anti-trappers to influence my life?

Some oldtimers say game is less plentiful now than in "the old days" (as though fluctuation in numbers was an abnormal occurrence) but I doubt that anyone really knows. Most such recollections suffer from the absence of any written notes and the unreliability of memory. Like all other habitats, this valley is capable of supporting a certain population of wildlife and I doubt that the habitat was ever much more productive than now. There is less of it, however, and the hunting is not so good as it used to be. The biologists say the "success ratio" is down. That is a technocrat's way of saying that one has to hunt longer to get an animal than used to be the case. I am of the opinion that this may result more from larger numbers of hunters than smaller numbers of deer. It is likely a combination of many things.

Deer and elk numbers are increasing of late but that may be due more to a series of mild winters than anything else. This is deep snow country and in normal winters there are always some ungulates that starve to death. In severe winters these losses can be enormous. Logging low-elevation and south-facing slopes is beginning to create good wildlife habitat and, in such areas, populations are certain to rise. In the main, wildlife habitat losses in this valley have been quite dramatic. They dammed the Duncan River, causing the permanent loss of much winter range. And people continue to subdivide land, put up houses, house-trailers and fences. They clear more land, reducing wildlife cover and forage. The domestic dog population is on the increase as well. Most dogs will harass — even kill deer. So I suspect the increase in deer and elk numbers may be temporary and will certainly be adversely hit by the first severe winter. You can't stockpile them.

Although I work in the field of wildlife conservation, I don't think about hunting other times of the year but when fall comes, the urge is always there. It is one of several instinctive and seasonal urges, all somewhat the same. Replenish the woodpile, take in the garden, go hunting. Those other pastimes, while largely utilitarian, all have elements of pleasure associated with them, and so does hunting. As I said, there are many reasons for going.

I like to be out on those crisp autumn mornings. Before sunup is the best time. The frost turns the deep meadowgrass into a kind of shaggy tinsel. The blood from a heart-shot buck instantly steams for a while, then crystallizes. It has a kind of terrible beauty.

Things always seem a lot more quiet in the early morning. Even the nights have sounds. I think the pre-sunrise half-light is the most silent time of day and at such times, a gunshot is like a clap of nearby thunder. I will confess something, though. Our family has always had better luck in the evening hunts, especially for whitetail deer. The word "family" is stressed here. Twenty-five years ago, my wife and I took turns taking our pre-school son. We are taking our grandsons

76

now. But, of course, the hunting tradition is much broader than just one family or one set of meadows.

I recently modified a large-bore Marlin rifle for use in these thickets and meadows. Certainly, the building or modification of weapons for the hunt was one of the first physical skills developed by man — obviously another part of the hunting tradition.

There are people in British Columbia who can tell you (perhaps with dubious precision) just how much money is generated by hunting each year. The numbers are sometimes useful in defending wildlife management budgets or wildlife habitat against other choices. Of more significance are the statistics on how many of us hunters there actually are. In British Columbia, about 160,000 citizens (mostly heads of households) go hunting each year, mostly for meat they don't need. That total is made up of about 130,000 who purchase the British Columbia resident hunting licence and an estimated 30,000 others who prefer to hunt waterfowl, such as duck and geese, for which they must obtain a separate licence.

Hunter numbers are declining in British Columbia. When asked, the lapsed hunters said they quit because of cost, over-regulation, poor hunting and other reasons. Pressure from anti-hunters did not seem to be a factor. British Columbia has fewer hunters per capita than many Canadian provinces. New Brunswick has about one quarter of our population but the same number of hunters. In Newfoundland, the ratio is even higher. Yet wildlife management is a high priority with the governments of both those places. In British Columbia, it never has been. That is part of our tradition as well.

Politicians become accustomed to having most of their legislative initiatives opposed. Increasing budgets for wildlife would be praised from all quarters — what could be more "motherhood" than providing homes for those lovely animals? But generations of politicians of all parties continue to endure the pointed abuse of wildlife advocates rather than provide adequate wildlife management budgets, even though such would require only a trifling sum.

Unlike forestry, cattle grazing or fisheries management, the provincial Wildlife Branch almost pays its own way with the revenue derived from hunting licences, tags and other forms of taxation, being roughly equivalent to the amount spent on the resource. This money comes from big game guides, trappers and hunters.

In the absence of adequate management funding, dozens of wildlife management projects are now being undertaken and completed by volunteers, mostly hunters. More than 200 rod and gun clubs are located in all parts of British Columbia. Dozens of them, especially in the interior, engage in a wide variety of wildlife and habitat enhancement projects. These include such things as transplants of big game

77

animals to suitable (but vacant) habitats, prescribed forest burning to rehabilitate winter ranges, radio telemetry studies on many animal species, including mountain lion, mountain caribou and bighorn sheep. Some of these projects are carried out by the professionals of the provincial wildlife service but a growing number are actually done by hunter volunteers, with technical supervision provided by the professionals. Thus, hunter organizations are now doing direct, hands-on management. Using their labour and their funds to take up some of the slack created by inadequate government funds is now becoming part of the hunting tradition, also.

There is no denying that the hunter derives pleasure and excitement from the hunt. Those who try to convince you otherwise are being less than honest. I prefer wild meat to tame but if I could buy elk meat in a store it would not be the same. Filling the freezer is only a part of the reason for the survival of the hunting tradition.

It seems that this tradition has many components, including a (perhaps inherited) extension of our ancestors' reliance on hunting, the many social aspects, and even the ability to provide a direct link with a more self-reliant past. I also believe that the conservation of wildlife is more likely to occur if the hunting tradition continues.

In our immediate family, each of us would have to hunt about 15 days in order to expect to make a kill. Provincially, the so-called "success ratio" is about one in four. Many big game hunters go for years without firing a shot. In most cases, killing an animal is no fluke but the result of days, even weeks, of effort and planning. I know hunters who rehearse their hunts, on the scene where they will ultimately occur. There are people who spend weeks scouting an area or even a specific animal and, perhaps, long before the season opens. The dedicated trophy hunter is in this category and I know people who have passed up making a kill for several years in order to wait for the one animal that suits them.

The personal rewards derived by a successful hunter are many. They include the obvious satisfaction of being able to provide at least a portion of the family food as a direct result of one's own labour. For most of us, the only one of life's necessities we can still obtain on our own is the air we breathe.

In actual fact, the attempt to separate hunting for meat from hunting for pleasure is almost pointless. Either reason is good enough; neither more important than the other. That it gives people pleasure to hunt is one of the reasons they do it. The meat is certainly the most healthy available, containing fewer chemicals than anything you can buy in stores. The assertion that we should hunt only for food and not for recreation seems to reject one component of the tradition and retain another, an event that I suspect does not reduce the number of animals killed. It also appears to be more of an urban concept, smacking of some fundamentalist interpretations of waste-not, want-not, rather than profound appreciation of the impact of hunting on a population of wildlife.

The main impact of hunting occurs with the killing of the animal, not what is done with the carcass afterward. It may also be ecologically unsound to contend that if a meat product does not pass through a human gut that constitutes waste. The anti-trophy hunters are particularly prone to this assumption. A strong ecological case could be made for leaving as much of the animal as possible in the habitat from which it emerged as this would provide direct benefit to scavenging species in the habitat, which would feed on its remains. Even without the hunter, that would be the natural fate of that biomass in any case. Such questions, however, are seldom discussed from a rational or scientific point of view. The height of passion and emotion that surrounds them simply prevents it.

It is also interesting that any discussion of the hunting tradition seems to provoke different responses from the rural person and the townsman. The advocating of universal standards of behaviour, regardless of one's location, is an uninformed presumption and certain to cause social disruption and protest. As stated, British Columbia is a highly diverse community and activities which might be totally appropriate in one setting might be quite inappropriate in another. One can fly from Vancouver to Fort Ware in three hours but the lifestyles are half a century apart. If a person drove into your yard (in Point Grey) with a rifle in the back window of his pickup, that might result in a call to police. In my yard, it would be surprising if a visitor did not have a gun in his truck — particularly in hunting season.

In the last seventy-five years, most of the hunting done by several generations of our extended family has occurred within two miles of this house. Several members of the family (both male and female) are active hunters, as are many of the neighbours. The few people who oppose it locally are from someplace else. No doubt our grandsons have eaten as much wild meat as tame, and they certainly prefer it. We all consider ourselves fortunate to be able to perpetuate the family hunting tradition. We regard it as a great privilege. Also a right.

There is a fine tradition of manners and social standards associated with hunting. It extends well beyond the matters of safe gun handling and respect of private property. In recent years, it has been offset by the actions of a few slobs. Responsible hunter organizations have countered by including in their outdoor activity, participation in hunter "patrols" in which organized hunters leave printed cards on truck windshields and in hunting camps to make people aware that slobs and game violators are not wanted and will be reported. The B.C. Wildlife Federation, parent body of organized hunters in British

Columbia, has paid thousands of dollars in reward money to persons reporting game violators and vandals. Increasingly, the image of the hunter must become a greater part of the consciousness of all who follow the sport, particularly at the local level.

Excepting a few local examples, we face no crisis in game populations in British Columbia. Some numbers are down and others higher than they have been for decades. Of the four endangered species in British Columbia, none is hunted; none is a game animal. More elk were shot in the East Kootenays in 1985 than existed in the entire population in 1965. Such events are not accidental but the result of planned and deliberate management programs, intended to protect and enhance animals and habitat. It works.

Locally, and in most parts of the province, there are the inevitable rises and dips in numbers as the animals respond to such things as severe winters or mild ones, to habitat alteration and, of course, to hunting pressure. On a province-wide basis, deer, the most abundant and frequently hunted of our big game animals, are down in numbers over a twenty-year average. Deer management must obviously become a higher priority if those numbers are to be restored. But while the deer numbers are obviously down across the province, I note that many of the hunting places used by my wife's father (and subsequent generations) continue to produce meat for the family table after decades of hunting. At the base of a certain spruce tree is a favourite deer stand overlooking a game trail that has been in use for more than fifty years. That represents three generations of hunters (in the same family) and about twelve or fifteen generations of whitetail deer, most of which were no doubt related as well.

In general terms and depending on the region, British Columbia wildlife populations are depressed in some places, on the increase in many, are in need of more intensive management in most, and, in some cases, we should likely be hunting them harder. Where we manage them best, the populations are the most healthy and viable. Where we do otherwise, they are usually in worse condition, whether we hunt them or not.

A lot of strong statements about hunting are made without the benefit of either experience or hard information. People oversimplify. And the enthusiasm one feels for a particular cause increases the risk of exaggeration in order to be convincing. All of us can recall being so tempted at times. Some anti-hunters seem to contend that a hunted population is automatically threatened and an unhunted population is automatically secure, an assumption that ignores the vital habitat connection. There is no doubt that individual animals may be threatened by the presence of the hunter — that is the whole purpose of the hunt — to select an animal and kill it, but a quite different situation applies with animal populations. The healthiest populations are those where numbers and habitat are in an appropriate balance.

Some hunters, sensitized by the anti-hunting faction, have resorted to some silly euphemisms to describe their hunting. Some hunters refer to killing an animal as "taking" it, as though the two were going for a stroll together. This overreaction cheapens the experience of hunting and plays into the hands of the anti-hunting minority.

On the north end of Kootenay Lake, where I live, deer hunting pressure is so high that limited entry hunting is in effect. But on the south end of the lake, deer are so numerous that in the mid-eighties, fruit growers were given permission to night-hunt them with lights. Special seasons were opened but hunters could not reduce the deer numbers sufficiently. Logistics ruled out trapping and translocation. Orchard damage was reportedly quite severe. This contrast in deer populations occurred within the same valley and only eighty miles apart. In actual fact, the north Kootenay Lake population (though smaller) is likely the healthier of the two. Numbers appear to be well within the support capability of the habitat, and agriculture damage is not severe.

One cannot fairly assess the health of any wildlife population by a numbers count alone. We can have too few wild animals. We can also have too many. The process that seeks to strike a balance between animal numbers and available habitat is called wildlife management. Wildlife management can benefit from the properly regulated presence of the hunter.

It was the recognition of the dangers of over-population and the need for wildlife management that moved pioneer biologist and forester Aldo Leopold to observe, "The deer lives in fear of the lion; the mountain lives in fear of the deer." In the most drastic situations, the effects of overpopulation suggest more serious impacts than overhunting because the former threatens the actual environment on which the animals depend. Disease and die-off in wildlife populations are ghastly to behold. The grim prospect of heavy winter kill is equally horrible. When populations get too large, the animals can literally eat themselves out of house and home. The same situation can exist when severe winters force them into marginal forage conditions. We see manifestations of this circumstance when fruit growers request and receive permission to shoot public deer to protect private apple trees.

Hunting should not occur if it presents a threat to wildlife populations, but, if it does not, there are many sound, biological reasons why it should continue. Wildlife conservation is now a major part of the hunting tradition as well.

But enough of this soul-searching. It is now late afternoon. Across the meadows and thickets of this mountain valley a wild autumn storm is building. The south wind is slamming against the shaked gables of this house. This is going to be a violent evening. The grasses and sedges are heeled over in the wind and the clouds have closed down darkly. There is no more perfect time to be hunting these meadows than now. This is another, much less theoretical part of the hunting tradition. I am about to revisit the same hunting places in which generations of family members have hunted before me, where, hopefully, generations to come will hunt as well.

Whether by instinct, conditioning, intelligence or some combination of them all, the local whitetail deer have learned that nocturnal or twilight times are the safest periods to feed. For the most part, they are late evening and early morning movers. Crepuscular.

Spooked and suspicious, the bucks shun the dark timber during these hammering storms. They seem to dislike the rattle and snap of overhead limbs on the forested sidehills. The wind signals cannot be trusted and there is all sorts of stuff falling down. So they tend to haunt the edge of their thicket and meadow habitat, the so-called ecotone. There, in the gusty windswirl, they can quickly forage enough food to fill their rumens. In this kind of abundant meadow, it takes only about half an hour. Then, they can lie down in the long grass and chew their cuds and rest till the morning feed, snug below the line of the wind. We see their beds in the morning.

In this setting, they must be taken in that brief interlude of feeding time. On such days it is often the only time there is. The preparations are practiced and routine. Warm mackinaw, cap, gloves, binocular, gun, shells and knife. There are many deer in this valley. Many deer on this place. Whitetail deer. They are out there now. I can feel them. It's time to go.

*"(Biology) is the least self-centered, the least narcissistic of the sciences —
the one that, by taking us out of ourselves, leads us to re-establish a link
with nature and to shake ourselves free from our spiritual isolation."*

Jean Rostand
Can Man Be Modified?

Increasingly, wildlife scientists are learning more and more about the animals with which we share this province. This quest for knowledge goes all the way back in our history to a naturalist who sailed with Captain Cook in 1778. A parade of scientists and naturalists followed but it wasn't until 1947, a mere 40 years ago, that the province appointed a trained scientist to its wildlife staff.

Today there are dozens of professionally trained scientists in the wildlife branch and the ministry's regional offices. By almost any measure it is as good a staff of wildlife scientists as there is in any province in Canada. It would be folly to say that we now know enough about wildlife. But it is simplistic to argue that our main problems are still technical in nature.

If wildlife management is largely people management, as many experienced managers will attest, then it would make sense to have some "people scientists" on board as well. To be sure many wildlife managers have become, in order to survive, pretty good people managers — the jack-knife variety — as opposed to professionally trained sociologists. But to our knowledge no province in Canada employs professionals in the humanities to help with the handling of people problems.

It would take a long chapter to cover the excellent work done by the scientists in government, in the provincial museum, and at the universities of the province. Their work is exciting and although always hampered by insufficient funding, they have made significant progress in wildlife management in British Columbia.

CHAPTER 6

Science and the Conservation of Wildlife in British Columbia

Ian McTaggart Cowan

The early history of wildlife management in British Columbia followed the classical European pattern. It was based on the control of hunting, the elimination of all kinds of predatory birds and mammals and the culture of exotic species of game birds.

Birds and mammals were important as a source of food to the Indian people and to the early colonists entering the province, but it was not long before deer and other larger species began to decrease in numbers under the steady assault, and the first legislation aimed at delaying the disappearance of the game species was enacted. This first wildlife conservation act was published in 1859 and prohibited the buying and selling of deer of any kind as well as ducks, teal, geese, woodcock, snipe, quail and grouse during stated periods between January and September. Thus wildlife conservation in our province had a niggardly birth based upon obviously declining populations under the impact of unrestricted killing.

For the next 50 years the general philosophy was one of parcelling out a dwindling supply of wildlife rather than one of maintaining and enhancing a renewable resource.

President Theodore Roosevelt of the United States of America is credited with promoting a new idea — conservation through wise use. He conceived of forest, rangeland, water and wildlife as renewable natural resources which could last forever if they were managed on the basis of scientifically gained information and used within the limits of their capacity for renewal.

The Roosevelt doctrine of conservation set the pattern for subsequent development of game management in North America. The principles of his doctrine were three: (Leopold, 1942)

1. It recognized all outdoor resources as an integral whole.
2. It recognized their conservation through wise use as a public responsibility and their private ownership as a public trust.
3. It recognized science as a tool for discharging that responsibility.

Today it is difficult to appreciate what a radical innovation this was. It represented a head-on confrontation with the existing dogma and introduced a new way of thinking, always a difficult task. It was resented and rejected by those who were unable to adapt to new concepts.

Seventy years later the scientific method is generally recognized as the appropriate approach to problems in wildlife conservation. It is the basis of all research on animal species and their habitats and much of that on human behaviour in the use of wildlife.

The scientific method deals with things that can be counted or measured in some way. It may be a census of bighorn on a winter range; the calories of energy to be derived from willow twigs eaten by moose; the annual growth rings in the canine of a grizzly or the mortality statistics of caribou under predation by wolves and grizzly. The method involves a) observation leading to the assembly of data, b) the development of an hypothesis that is the simplest testable explanation that includes all the observed facts, and c) testing the hypothesis by further critical observations, by logical deductions that must flow from the hypothesis, or by undertaking controlled experiments.

If the working hypothesis cannot stand the tests it must be discarded and a new one devised that recognizes the new body of data, and so on. Thus the process of scientific study of a topic includes data gathering, organization of the data, analysis, and interpretation of results leading to conclusions that have an acceptable degree of proof behind them. The final stage is reporting the results, along with the data and the analytical processes that led to the conclusion, so that others can examine them, repeat them and can apply the results to the solution of problems. This is the ideal sequence but frequently in this less than perfect world it eludes us.

Many problems that arise in wildlife management are difficult to reduce to testable hypotheses that can be subjected to experiment. Furthermore, the experiments that can be designed to apply under field conditions are so expensive, in money and in time, that much of the research on wildlife topics is observational in nature. It is a fact of life that most management decisions in wildlife conservation have to be based upon strong inference arising from careful observation.

The role of the scientist in the management of the wildlife resource is to design and undertake research, to keep abreast of the work of other researchers so that their findings can be applied to the solution of local problems or used in planning further research, and to advise the managers of the results of research so that they may be used to guide decisions. This also is easier to state than to achieve but ideal targets are important as goals to achievement.

These aspects of wildlife research and the role of the wildlife biologist are discussed in detail at many levels in the literature on research. A useful summary is given by Giles, 1969.

In the Beginning

The application of the scientific method to the study of wild creatures and their habitats is not much more than half a century old but it rests on a body of knowledge that goes back to the dawn of man's observation of the creatures with which he shared his habitat. The information was gained empirically through years of human survival. One can only marvel at the degree of detailed knowledge primitive man had gained. There were keen observers and clear reasoners among them.

The first question asked as explorer naturalists entered what is now British Columbia was, "What creatures inhabit this new land and how do they relate to creatures already known from elsewhere?" These questions could only be answered by the collecting of specimens for later examination by a specialist. Thus the amassing of the data required for scientific examination began with the first naturalists.

Most of the early naturalists to enter British Columbia were more interested in birds than in other wildlife. Thus William Anderson, the naturalist with James Cook's expedition of 1778, collected 15 species of birds at Nootka Sound. Seventy years elapsed before the next specimens were taken in the province. In 1858, Thomas W. Blakiston explored parts of the Flathead and Kootenay valleys and preserved specimens of four species of birds.

He was followed by John Keast Lord, the naturalist with the commission appointed to survey the boundary between the United States and Canada. Lord worked in British Columbia between 1860 and 1863 and listed 236 species of birds as well as collecting several species of mammals which he recorded in his rather disorganized book (1866).

By the late 1800's, there were resident naturalists in the province. Roderick MacFarland with the Hudson's Bay Company at Fort St. James; William E. Brooks and his son Allan arrived at Chilliwack in 1887; John Fannin was living on the shores of Burrard Inlet, and there were no doubt others whose contributions remain unknown because they did not publish their findings.

The government of the province founded the Provincial Museum in 1886 and appointed John Fannin as its first curator. In 1891, he published the first account of the birds of the entire province. This stirred widespread interest in the bird fauna of the region and, in the next few years, several expeditions came here to obtain specimens for the scientific collections of the major museums in the United States. Clark P. Streator in 1889 and 1896, Samuel N. Rhoads, 1892; J. Alden Loring, 1894; and Edward A. Preble in 1897 travelled widely in the province and made notable additions to the knowledge of the birds and mammals of British Columbia. As a result of their work and that of others the knowledge gained from many hundreds of specimens from British Columbia was included in the long series of synoptic studies of mammals and birds of North America published by the United States Natural Museum. These appeared in the 74 volumes of the North American Fauna Series as well as in the monumental 11-volume work by Ridgeway; *The Birds of North and Middle America* (1901-1941).

Through the first half of the twentieth century the detailed exploration of the provincial biota increased in intensity and changed in nature. No longer were field parties concentrating on building a catalogue of what was there. They were interested as much in geographic variation within the different species and documented the habitats occupied by the creatures as they collected representative series of specimens for statistical study. This innovation came largely from the University of California, Berkeley, where Joseph Grinnell, Director of the Museum of Vertebrate Zoology, had pioneered the quantitative approach to describing the evolution of sub-species by many birds and mammals in response to marked changes in the environment. At the same time, he and his colleagues began the analytical description of ecosystems.

The final expedition to British Columbia by the scientists of the United States Bureau of Biological Survey was that of Wilfred H. Osgood and Edmund Heller to the Queen Charlotte Islands. Their report (Osgood, 1901) is innovative in its description of plant associations related to the distribution of the birds and mammals.

In 1907 and 1909, Harry S. Swarth headed expeditions to the Sitkan district of southeast Alaska that included collecting birds and mammals along the Stikine River up as far as Telegraph Creek, B.C. In 1910, he and his colleagues spent five months studying the birds and mammals of Vancouver Island. Because Swarth did both the field work and the subsequent analysis of the data his studies made notable scientific contributions.

Almost all these field studies concentrated on the small mammals and the birds and paid scant attention to the large mammals. Almost no detailed work had been devoted to these culturally important species until Andrew J. Stone of Missoula, Montana, travelled to the Che-on-nee Mountains on the Stikine River following the trail of reports he had heard of a strange black mountain sheep inhabiting the area. He was successful in collecting three specimens of the sheep that now bears his name: the Stone's sheep *Ovis dalli stonei* (Allen,

1897). He returned in 1902 with an assistant and between July 8 and October 23 assembled the first collection made of the mammals of an area of mountainous northern British Columbia. Specimens taken included nine caribou, six moose, nine Stone's sheep, four mountain goats, two grizzly bear, one black bear and a wolf, all carefully prepared for scientific study. A monumental task.

Simultaneously, Charles Sheldon became fascinated by the wild sheep inhabiting the remote mountain ranges of Alaska and the Yukon. In 1904 and 1905, travelling alone, he penetrated most of the isolated mountainous areas of Yukon Territory lying to the east and north of the Yukon River from the Ogilvie Mountains south into northern British Columbia. He revealed that over this huge area the pure white sheep of Alaska intergrated with the black sheep of the Stikine. He published the results of this unique study in his wilderness classic *The Wilderness of the Upper Yukon*.

Another regional study of the early 1900's was that of Ned Hollister and J. H. Riley, both of the United States National Museum. They accompanied the Alpine Club Expedition to Mount Robson in the summer of 1911 and later reported on the birds and mammals of the region.

Private naturalist collectors played a most important role in the task of developing an inventory of the fauna of British Columbia and its distribution. Between 1887, when Allan Brooks arrived at Chilliwack with his father, and 1971 when private collecting of birds was terminated by the Canadian Wildlife Service, 17 naturalists collected and prepared for their own and future study about 30,000 specimens along with related field notes. At the same time they produced more than 100 published accounts of their findings. In addition, five of them together assembled several thousand specimens of mammals. Almost all these specimens are now in public museums where they have provided the source data for many scientific studies of the distribution, systematics and physical characteristics of provincial wildlife.

The largest private collections of birds and mammals were those of Allan Brooks, J. A. Munro, T. T. and E. B. McCabe, Kenneth Racey and the author.

Museum Years

The Provincial Museum, from its inception in 1886, has been important in ornithology and mammalogy, steadily building, cataloguing, and curating fine collections for reference and research.

Following his 1891 publication on the birds of the province, Fannin undertook further study and produced a revision in 1894. This was rewritten and brought up-to-date by Kermode in 1904. By 1925, much new information had been obtained and a new study was published by Brooks and Swarth.

This author was appointed to the Museum in 1935 as a biologist and served there for five years. During that time, field work on the distribution of the vertebrates was revived. At that time, I also made useful contacts within the Fish and Game Branch and began research on the ecology of the black-tailed deer assisted by a most interested and active game warden, Rex Hayes. While enforcing the game laws with impartiality and vigour he was eager for information on the lives of the creatures he protected. We had many adventures together.

In 1944, Munro and I collaborated to produce a new and expanded analysis of the provincial avifauna. This was followed in 1956 by a comprehensive handbook on the mammals of British Columbia by the author and Charles Guiguet of the Museum staff.

Information on the reptiles and amphibians was assembled by the author in 1937, and brought up-to-date by Carl in 1943 (Amphibia) and 1944 (Reptilia). Recently D. M. Green and R. Wayne Campbell did the same for the reptiles (1984). All these handbooks have been published by the Provincial Museum. Thus by the mid-thirties, there was a basic understanding of what vertebrates inhabited our province and how they were distributed.

The Museum has continued to fulfill its mandate as a major repository for the specimen collections that are the basis of knowledge of the presence of species and the details of their distribution. It has been active also in its collaboration with the Fish and Wildlife agency and other provincial offices that require information on the native fauna. Since 1945 it has shared this task with the Museum of Vertebrate Zoology at the University of British Columbia.

By 1965, Charles Guiguet and Wayne Campbell of the Museum staff were adding a population dimension to Museum research with their census studies of the marine bird nesting colonies along the coast of the province.

The Universities in Wildlife Science

In 1921, the province established the University of British Columbia. Since then the provincial universities have been at the centre of scientific activity and innovation. The Department of Zoology at U.B.C. came into being in 1923. The first Head of the Department, Charles McLean Fraser, came to the university from his previous position as Director of the Pacific Biological Station of the Fisheries Research Board of Canada at Departure Bay. Inevitably he brought with him a concern for the contribution that science could make to the management of the natural resources. He was a marine scientist and one of his early studies was an investigation of the impact of the

Steller's sea lion on the commercial fisheries of the Pacific coast of Canada. Fraser's colleague in the two-man department was George J. Spencer, entomologist and accomplished general naturalist.

Fraser retired in 1940 and was succeeded by Wilbur A. Clemens who had followed Fraser as Director of the Pacific Biological station. He invited me to leave the museum and to join him at the University at the identical salary I was getting in Victoria — $200 a month! This was a most exciting opportunity. I had completed my doctorate in zoology at the University of California under the guidance of the eminent vertebrate ecologist Joseph Grinnell and here was a chance to put my ideas and enthusiasm to work in teaching and research. I accepted the invitation promptly.

The University was a great place to work. It was small, growing, eager to innovate and was attracting able students. There were not enough hours in the day. Undergraduate and graduate courses in Vertebrate Zoology were soon designed and approved along with a curriculum leading to the Master's degree in that field.

The first student to receive a Master's degree at U.B.C. in the new field was Charles David Fowle of Vernon in 1944. He was followed in 1947 by James Hatter. The University of British Columbia had not yet embarked upon instruction leading to the Ph.D. degree and both of these first graduates went elsewhere for their doctoral studies, Fowle to Toronto and Hatter to Washington State University, where I was appointed to the faculty, on a dollar a year basis, to supervise his research on the biology of the moose in British Columbia. The expenses of this research were paid by the provincial Department of Fish and Game, beginning a long and fruitful collaboration between that Department and the University.

Hatter's thesis, "The Moose of Central British Columbia" (1950) was the first major study of a wildlife species in the province. My 1945 publication on the ecological relationship of the food of the Columbian black-tailed deer was the first ecological study of a British Columbian mammal. An even earlier first in research on British Columbia wildlife was Munro's 1923 publication on birds as predators on spawning salmon on Vancouver Island.

These were "heady" days for those interested in the study of birds and mammals and their conservation. In Europe and North America a new "breed" of scientist had taken to the field and was applying scientific methods to exploring their curiosity about creatures and their habitats. There was an explosion of new knowledge.

Frank Fraser Darling had written *A Herd of Red Deer* (1936), the first scientific inquiry into the behaviour of a large mammal. A year later, Aldo Leopold published his book *Game Management* which broke new ground and stimulated the science-based approach to wildlife management and conservation. Margaret M. Nice published the first of

91

her ingeniously analytical studies of a population of song sparrows. Nikko Tinbergen (1939) was developing his experimental approach to the study of animal social organization. Charles Elton in 1942 published his classic study on animal populations in *Mice, Voles and Lemmings.*

The North American Wildlife Conference was convened first in 1936. Its published proceedings included symposia on upland wildlife research, wildlife disease, population cycles research, forests and forest wildlife, and water pollution and wildlife. One paper dealt with the heavy winter losses experienced by the moose on Isle Royal in the absence of both hunting and predation. Another landmark paper in this publication was by H. L. Stoddard on "The Relation of Burning to Timber and Wildlife." This was the first step in what has been many years of study of the role of forest fires in the ecology of productive forests and of wildlife habitat.

There were just two Canadian research papers presented at this international conference. W. E. Swales of McDonald College presented a short paper on parasites of wildlife species and R. E. DeLury invoked sun spot cycles to explain cyclical changes in wildlife populations. Wildlife research was in its infancy here and the so-called 12-year cycle in numbers of many species was challenging the few biologists in the field. Norman Criddle of Manitoba had published his observation on the fluctuation of ruffed grouse and C. H. D. Clarke addressed the same phenomenon in his 1936 doctoral thesis at the University of Toronto.

Today, 50 years later, the explanation is still being sought by a team of scientists from U.B.C., University of Alberta and University of Toronto combining their efforts in Yukon where the phenomenon is a dominating attribute of populations of snowshoe hares, lynx, grouse, ptarmigan, lemmings and other voles, ermine, marten, snowy owls and some other species.

The Wildlife Society had been formed in the United States and in 1937 it had published the first volume of the Journal of Wildlife Management. This volume, of 107 pages, contained 11 articles. Six of them had strong habitat orientation; all but two of them involved the use of population figures. Already the input of research data had moved thinking away from the early preoccupation with predation and hunting kill, to a broader interest in the role of the total environment in the maintenance of healthy populations of wildlife species.

In the 1950's, the explosive growth of the universities created a demand for more faculty and several of those added were vertebrate zoologists. Over the years Miklos D. F. Udvardy, James Bendell, John Krebs, Charles Krebs, Dennis Chitty, Jamie Smith, Harold Nordan, H. Dean Fisher, Anthony Sinclair, J. Mary Taylor and C.

Lee Gass taught in the Department of Zoology at U.B.C., undertook research upon birds or mammals, and guided the work of graduate students for longer or shorter periods.

But the study of wildlife species has broad contacts in science, and several areas of the university participated. Vernon C. Brink in Plant Science and A. J. Wood in Animal Science were deeply involved with research and in the training of graduate students, frequently in co-operation with zoologists. There was interest also among students in Forestry and in 1971, Fred Bunnell was hired as a full-time wildlife biology professor in the Faculty of Forestry. He has had an important impact in the complex area of the management of forests in the joint interest of producing trees and wildlife.

In total, between 1945 and 1985, the University of British Columbia has awarded post graduate degrees in various aspects of wildlife biology to about 160 students. They have become faculty members at universities throughout Canada as well as in Alaska and in several of the southern 48 states, in Finland, Norway and Africa. They have entered the federal civil service to serve as scientists and administrators. In the provincial governments from the Atlantic to the Pacific, and in Yukon and Northwest Territories they have served at various levels from biologist to deputy minister. They have been active in the revolution that has swept the practice of wildlife management in Canada over the past 40 years.

Beginning in 1978, Simon Fraser University entered the field with the appointment of Nikko Verbeek joined later by Alton Harested. The University of Victoria has granted graduate degrees with specialization in vertebrate biology under the direction of E. M. Hagmeier since 1967 and more recently has had the services of Patrick T. Gregory and Tom Bergerud.

The research accomplished by this parade of faculty and graduate students at the universities has roamed widely over the very rich field represented by wildlife biology. Some of their studies attacked problems demanding immediate solution. Others had a longer term objective and sought to build deeper understanding of the creatures we wish to conserve.

The Provincial Game Commission

This title is used as the one of longest life among the several designations borne by the office responsible for the management of the wildlife resource of the province.

In the 1930's, the provincial Game Commission had survived its early history as a political football. For many years the structure of the agency responsible for managing the game and sports fish resources of the province changed with the election fortunes of the two major

political parties. When one political philosophy prevailed this responsibility was given to the provincial police. But when fortune favoured
the other party there was a separate agency with its own administration and enforcement arm. The profound differences between managing a living resource and policing the users escaped the understanding of those of more conservative political bent. However, even
if the lawmakers were sometimes confused about the significant
differences in philosophy, the provincial Game and Forest Warden,
as the senior game administrator was called until 1913, indicates in
his reports that he sensed the differences. His report of 1908, as an
example, pays far more attention to the numerical status of the
different game species, and to attempts to introduce exotic species to
supplement local ones than it does to law enforcement.

After about twenty years of trial and error, the late 1930's saw the
task of protecting wildlife and fish in British Columbia placed in the
hands of co-commissioners who reported directly to the Attorney
General. This arrangement continued to express the philosophy that
the tasks were largely of a law enforcement nature.

The two commissioners, Frank R. Butler and James G. Cunningham administered five regions each headed by an Inspector. Within
each region there were several game wardens. Their duties included
enforcing the game act and its regulations and similarly the fisheries
regulations in non-tidal water. They were also expected to know how
the game creatures in their districts were faring. Very few of them had
any interest in natural history or in the host of birds and mammals
that were not considered game, except those hawks, eagles, owls,
crows, magpies, jays, coyotes, wolves and cougars that were marked
for destruction as pests.

The setting of hunting regulations was a reasonably democratic
process involving advice from the game wardens based upon their
impressions of the numbers of the different species in their areas.
Another series of recommendations went to the commissioners from
the sportsmen's organization, also based on guesswork.

When the wildlife biologist appeared on the scene he had techniques for estimating the numbers of a species along with sex and age
ratios and other important details. He could provide these figures
with a statistically calculated statement of the limits within which his
estimates were accurate. He could determine birth rates, survival
rates, losses to predators, disease, and starvation. He could measure
plant cover; the proportion of the vegetation that was being used; the
nutritional value of the different feeds available; the changes taking
place in the habitats and the probable consequences to the animal
species. The informed guess was no longer an acceptable basis for
wildlife management decisions. A new source of information was

available that was closer to reality and could be used to refine management practices.

Equally important, the biologists were trained in how and where to search the literature for the research findings of others elsewhere which had a bearing upon their own concerns. They were windows on a new world.

Most sportsmen were genuinely interested in the wild creatures that they saw and hunted. The new information made available to them by the biologists increased their enjoyment of their days afield.

In 1940, British Columbia was ready for the change to science-based management of its wildlife resources. But a civil service system cannot be changed in a day. Even it it could have been, biologists were in short supply.

Commissioner Butler was an innovator. Already he had devised and installed in the province the Registered Trapline System demonstrating his understanding of the renewability of the wildlife resource. It was the most important innovation in wildlife management of its day. Its success led him to adopt the same principle in instituting the block guiding districts. This removed the big game guiding business from the cut-throat competition that threatened the populations of some of our most spectacular species. In 1930, Butler and Cunningham sensed what Garrett Hardin, 20 years later, referred to as the "Tragedy of the Commons," and had devised ways of avoiding the problem in two areas of their responsibility.

As early as 1935, the Fish and Game Commissioners were developing links with the biological scientists in the province. D. C. B. Duff of the Department of Bacteriology at the University of British Columbia helped the Commissioners solve some problems of diseases in the provincial trout hatcheries. W. A. Clemens of the Departure Bay biological station gave advice on fish management problems as did Charles Mottley.

From the time of our arrival on the university campus Clemens and I enjoyed friendly relationships with Butler and Cunningham and with most of the inspectors. To an increasing extent we were asked for advice on a wide variety of fish and game problems. Co-operative programs were arranged under which university students were guided into research studies of immediate concern to the Game Commissioners who provided the funding for the studies which served also as thesis projects for the students.

In 1950, a more formal relationship was forged when we were appointed as honorary scientific advisors to the Commission. The University made us available as much as possible to travel to the regional headquarters to advise the inspectors and the wardens. It was a busy and strenuous life with seven-day weeks commonplace, but it was fascinating. We were in constant demand from the sportsmen's groups, to lecture or to take part in discussions. We gave dozens of lectures in all parts of the province. All this helped to spread the "gospel" of science and facilitated the transition of the game administration to the new mode.

Scientifically trained individuals were hired by the Commission as they graduated from the university. The first was James Hatter, in 1947. He was attached to the headquarters in Vancouver as a staff biologist and was encouraged to complete his Ph.D. This he achieved in 1950.

In 1949, Ernest Taylor joined, with the special assignment of studying the biology and management of the pheasant. The same year the first major organizational change occurred when the Commission established a Scientific Branch with Clemens and myself as scientific advisors, Hatter as the game biologist, P. A. Larkin as fish biologist, Stewart Smith as assistant fish biologist, W. Winston (Bill) Mair as Supervisor of Predatory Animal Control, and Ernest Samann as his assistant. A year later a new crop of graduate students completed their Master's degrees and Donald J. Robinson and Patrick W. Martin were hired as assistant biologists. The addition of Lawson Sugden in 1953 as range management biologist and Glen Smith as regional biologist in the East Kootenay completed the roster. The Game Commission was now equipped to obtain the scientific information it needed from all major areas of the province except the far north.

The new biologists fitted well into the existing system. Many of the men were not only recent university graduates, they had served in Canada's armed forces in Europe and brought with them a sense of maturity that was helpful to the tasks at hand. All of them were hunters, fishermen and naturalists with a lot of outdoor experience. They were a pretty select lot. At the same time they appreciated the extensive local knowledge and "woods wisdom" that some of the wardens had and were eager to learn.

The introduction of all these new "experts" inevitably ruffled a few feathers in the existing establishment. Not all the newcomers were paragons of diplomacy, and some of the wardens left much to be desired and were difficult for eager idealistic biologists to tolerate. However, in retrospect it is remarkable how well this territorial friction was kept under control.

At this time the problems seen as most pressing were:

1. The explosive expansion in distribution and numbers of the moose in central British Columbia.
2. Declining pheasant populations and the annual demand from the sportsmen for the release of more farm-raised birds to supplement the wild stock.

A stage coach used by early game officers in the central interior of British Columbia.

In 1899, you could buy a Free Miner's Certificate . . . and all the game you could shoot for $4.

A. Bryan Williams was the first game warden in British Columbia. His annual reports are still fascinating reading.

Bringing in some of the several thousand pheasants that were released in the lower mainland at the turn of the century.

The Cache Creek game check station in the later 1940's.

European immigrants welcomed the opportunity to hunt from the commons. Attesting to his prowess, this hunter and his grandson proudly pose with the result of a day's hunt. PHOTO COURTESY NEVIS DEMARCHI, 1951

Glen Smith, the first government biologist in the Kootenays, and his dog Chucker.

The 1938 Convention of the Interior Fish and Game Protective Association, Kamloops, June 2nd.

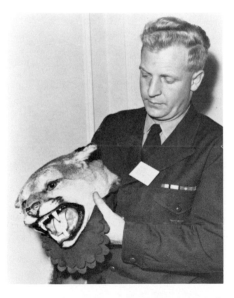

TRAPLINE MARKED IN RED.
CHEIF louie GEORGE   MucHalat RESERVE
ABOUT 80 MILES.   NOOTKA BC
JUNE 7th 1928.
THIS AppliCATION is for THE wHole
of THE MucHalaT BAND inCluDING.
CHEIF Louie GEORGE.
M TOMMY AA Ioyeious. M.Bob. Napolion. DODOk
J. THOMAS. M. PETER. A. Joseph. A.A. MuGrom
H. Francis. MARCUS. Abel JOHN.   UCONA RIVER
Alec Bob. M. Joe. PETER JACKSON.
and Jacob Louie

TulpaH ARM

49°50'   49°50'
49°45'   49°45'
49°40'   49°40'
Bright
1510

GAMPO BAY

MUCHAIaT ARM.

Map. No. 2 C.

126°30'   126°20'   126°10'   126°

The development of registered traplines was a major advance in resource management in Canada. It started in B.C. with the participation of the trappers themselves.

Al West, Supervisor of predator control, holds what many people thought was the only good use for a cougar — a floor mat.

Two legends in B.C.'s wildlife management story — Frank R. Butler (left) and
James G. Cunningham.

Frank R. Butler, director of the Fish and Game branch, points
out a trouble spot to Jim Hatter (centre), later to follow Butler
as director, and Al West, supervisor of predator control.

3. Wolves, coyotes and cougars as predators on big game and domestic livestock.
4. The collapse of the continental waterfowl population.
5. Wildlife damage to crops, as agriculture spread ever farther onto marginal lands hitherto wildlife habitat.
6. The unstable population of bighorn sheep, which every few years was wracked by disease.
7. The effects upon deer and grouse of clearcutting and burning forest lands on Vancouver Island.

The first biologists were busy people, and quickly learned that the demands of the job seldom provided the time required to do a fully satisfying job on any task before another one was handed to them. But they coped. In day-to-day operations they soon were required to devote much of their time to many small problems with which their knowledge and approach were useful. Inevitably the continued research effort required to arrive at satisfactory answers to important questions went by default. There simply was not the time to devote to it or the money to pay for it.

The close working relationship between the University and the Game Department culminated in 1962 with the establishment at the University of the research offices of the Game Commission. This arrangement was mutually advantageous. The Game administration got access to the University library and to the wealth of research laboratories and their specialist staffs as well as the opportunity to recruit students to their research tasks. The University gained assistance with the financing of graduate student research and in the guidance of research students. The arrangement worked well for many years with John Bandy serving as wildlife research officer and Peter Larkin and Tom Northcote in the fisheries laboratory.

Research Glimpses

Much fascinating research was conducted by the combined team of University and Game Commission scientists and the graduate students. Some projects were short-term and directed to the immediate solution of "practical" questions. Some tackled more complex problems that required many years of effort. Indeed some of them are still the subject of continuing research. A few examples will suggest the scope and variety of the studies.

In the late 1940's, the fruit growers of the Okanagan Valley in their attack on insect pests turned from heavy metal sprays to the newly developed products such as Parathion, D.D.T., Lindane and Hexafoss. The new pesticides had advantages in cost of labour and materials and appeared to give satisfactory control. However, there was little appreciation of their hazard to the user or to birds and mammals living in the orchards. Very soon there was a noticeable decline in the numbers of pheasants in and around the orchards. Sportsmen and naturalists suspected the new sprays.

In 1949, Arthur Benson studied the problem as his research toward the Master's degree at U.B.C. His research questions were: a) Do the sprays kill the pheasants? and, b) If they do, what evidence is there that they are responsible for the decline in the pheasant numbers?

Benson's research involved exposing pheasant chicks and their bantam foster mothers to the sprays being applied in commercial orchards. Two regimes were used. Some pens of experimental birds were placed in the orchards just before the sprayer went by and were immediately removed to clean ground. These birds were thus exposed only to the inhalation of the spray for the few minutes it was in the atmosphere. A second group of birds was kept out of the orchard during the spraying but then placed in pens on the sprayed area. These birds did not inhale the spray but were exposed to it as they ate vegetation and insects contaminated by it. A third group was used as a control and was at no time exposed to the spray chemicals.

The results were dramatic and unequivocal. All four of the chemicals tested caused the rapid death of the birds. Inhalation was the more quickly lethal. Mature birds seemed to be more susceptible to death from contaminated food than the chicks.

Despite the high mortality of the pheasants from the sprays being used, other evidence led to the conclusion that spray deaths were not the ultimate cause of the decline in numbers. The problem appeared to arise from major changes in cultural practices in the orchards, notably a change from ditch irrigation to the use of large overhead sprinklers. Along with this was the increased mowing of the ground cover. These practices together made the orchards and adjacent agricultural land less suitable for pheasant nesting and brood raising. Of course, the spray was reducing the populations even further.

Another interesting problem was brought to the University in 1972. The airport at Port Hardy was encountering problems with bald eagles as a hazard to aircraft landing and taking off. The main runway had been built so that the southeast end was just short of the Keogh River. This river attracted important runs of coho, pink and chum salmon between September and December that brought in large numbers of eagles. These birds, in flying up and down the river in pursuit of salmon, crossed the flight path of the aircraft.

James T. Cuthbert studied the problem for his Master of Science degree. Reduced to its essentials there were several possible solutions. For example, it was theoretically possible to eliminate the eagles or the salmon, or to alter the direction of the runway so that it avoided the river and its hazards. Each of these potential solutions was unacceptable for a number of reasons. Cuthbert gathered data on the flight path taken by the incoming and outgoing aircraft on dozens of landings. He also took hundreds of measurements of the flight paths of the eagles during the time the salmon were present. His preferred solution was to raise the flight path of the aircraft so that it was above that used by the eagles most of the time. This could be done by lengthening the runway at the end away from the river by some 610 metres.

This recommendation was carried out, along with some others that together reduced the hazard to an acceptable level.

Many research tasks produced results that led to changes in regulations or in wildlife management practices. James Hatter's pioneering research on the moose in British Columbia, conducted between 1945 and 1949, documented the dramatic increase in moose numbers beginning in the 1920's. Moose spread southward from the Stikine and Peace river drainages through the entire central region of the province and even as far as the international boundary. As they did so, region after region experienced eruptions in moose numbers. These led to overbrowsing of the vegetation and to a subsequent decline in the number of animals that began in 1938.

One conclusion of this research was that it was important to adjust the numbers of moose to the carrying capacity of the environment. The way to do this was to arrange for the removal of cows as well as bulls from the population. This did violence to the long-standing dogma that only the bulls or antlered animals should be hunted and resulted in several years of controversy. This involved some whose concerns were thoughtful, such as trapper Eric Collier, and others with a vested interest in the status quo. A leader in the latter group was caught by game wardens with a doe deer and a cow moose in his possession out of season and he garnered a heavy fine along with loss of credibility! However, the Commissioners accepted the recommendation, and either sex hunting was introduced to the province in 1952. It has been used from time to time as a management technique for moose, wapiti, and deer ever since then.

In the course of his research on the pheasants of the Fraser River Delta area, E. W. Taylor discovered that the release of farm-raised pheasants in the late summer to bolster the wild stock was not achieving the objective. Only five percent of the cock pheasants shot in the fall hunt were ranch-raised birds. Furthermore, almost none of the birds, cocks or hens, released in the late summer survived the winter to take their places as part of the nesting population. Several changes were made in attempts to improve the contribution of these hand-reared birds to increasing the numbers of pheasants available. None of them were successful and in 1954 the releasing of farm-reared birds was abandoned as uneconomic and ineffectual. Taylor's research had revealed that a practice long found successful on the intensively managed farms and coppices of Britain was not appropriate to the conditions in British Columbia. Over the years many thousands of dollars had been spent in rearing and releasing thousands of pheasants before it was subject to careful scrutiny through research.

A third practice long revered by the "practical" game managers, the payment of bounties for the destruction of all predatory birds and mammals, was also a casualty to research findings. After about a quarter of a million birds had been killed, the bounties on hawks, eagles, owls, crows and magpies were gradually eliminated between 1924 and 1931, largely through the influence of J. A. Munro, the Federal Migratory Bird Officer. Payment of bounties on coyotes, wolves, and cougars hung on until at least 1956. Their abandonment as a management practice is an example of the role of the biologist as a window on relevant research work world-wide. Although only limited study of the biology of predation was conducted in British Columbia, important research was going on elsewhere, notably that of Paul Errington of the University of Iowa, and F. C. Edminster of New York State.

It was shown that in British Columbia bounties were ineffectual in achieving the elimination of the individual predators that were doing demonstrable damage. Furthermore, the bounty system was open to fraudulent practices that were costing money that could be better spent on other forms of wildlife management.

Private Research

During the 1970's it became obvious that the rapid increase in access to the hitherto remote northern third of the province and the expanding industrial activity in the region had removed the protection the caribou, moose, Stone's sheep, mountain goat, grizzly and other creatures of this remarkable region had enjoyed. Signs of growing problems with the wildlife populations were apparent but the provincial government was unable to allocate the resources needed to study the problems and devise effective management strategies.

The need was for intensive research on a wilderness wildlife ecosystem involving a complex of large hoofed animals and their predators, including man.

The need was so urgent that a group of us organized the Spatsizi Association for Biological Research to design and conduct the research in Spatsizi Wilderness Park, an area that seemed to us to be representative of the larger region.

A group of university and government scientists outlined eight major, but co-ordinated, field research projects. Three of these focused on the caribou and moose and a fourth study involved the ecology of the wolf and its impact of the large prey animals.

Studies of this kind are very expensive and despite help from several sources we were only able to fund one major project through a five-year period — that on the population of caribou, its seasonal movements, its reproductive success and related topics. This was undertaken mainly by David Hatler (1986) but there were other research projects of a supporting nature conducted by provincial parks and wildlife biologists. The results, especially those obtained from caribou which were provided with radio collars, were fascinating.

It is unfortunate that the full sequence of studies could not be carried out. What was done has required us to revise our concepts of caribou local populations, their movements and mortality rates. It has also contributed further detail to our understanding of the role of the wolf in the complex relationship of predators and large ungulates in northern Brtish Columbia which has been the focus of John Elliott's research since 1977.

Among the many notable long-term studies were those carried on in the province on wild sheep by V. Geist, Darryl Hebert, V. C. Brink and his students, and now by Peter Davidson. Central to the studies has been the puzzle of the periodic epizootics that kill large numbers of bighorn sheep along the west side of the Rocky Mountains. Piece by piece the painstaking work of a succession of scientists is developing an understanding of the biology of these remarkable animals and of the die-offs they experience. This is suggesting ways in which it may be possible to prevent or ameliorate the severe losses that devastate some of the herds.

James Bendell and his colleagues have undertaken one of the longest continuous studies of an animal population in their research on blue grouse. Their data extend over 37 years and involve some interesting field experiments. Bendell has learned that this forest grouse moves each year from its winter range in the alpine conifer forests to the open lowland areas to nest. It is one of the few species that finds its most favourable breeding environments in the vast areas of clear cut or burned forests at lower elevations.

Here in newly cutover and burned areas its population increases manyfold and maintains high levels that are not cyclic until regrowth of the forest shades the forest floor and alters the nutritional content of the green plants required by the nesting females. It is clear also that predation is not a factor in population density on Vancouver Island.

This combination of life history features means that it is most difficult to manage a blue grouse population with the objective of increasing or prolonging its productivity. Yet the species survives well at low densities over very large areas.

Forty years of research by many biologists in British Columbia

101

have produced some major contributions to our knowledge of the great diversity of wildlife species that make up our fauna. It has provided a general understanding of the ecology of most of the large ungulates and many of the carnivores. For them the knowledge gained permits study of still more precise questions. As a result, those entrusted with the conservation and management of the wild vertebrates of the province can make their decisions with better knowledge and more confidence.

In the constant tension that exists between wildlife conservation and commercial timber harvests, expanding agriculture, flooding of valleys for hydro-electric power generation and other forms of "development," the knowledge gained by research on our wildlife species makes it easier to prepare the case for maintaining the habitat needed by our fauna.

In British Columbia today the wildlife resource is cared for by 110 professional staff of the Ministry of Environment and Parks as biologists, conservation officers and habitat protection officers. Forty years ago there were 59 game wardens and five predatory animal hunters involved. Many of the wardens had some police training but none of them had attended college or university.

In 1986, there were 135,128 licensed hunters in the province. In 1947, there were 55,700. In the forty years that have elapsed since the wildlife biologists brought science and technology to the task of conserving wildlife species on the basis of estimates of numbers, trends in abundance, reproductive rates, population turnover rates and habitat needs, there have been vast changes in the environment. Today, close to seventy percent of the forest land in the province has been cut or burned or devastated by insect attack; thousands of miles of "resource" roads have been built into hitherto natural "reserve" areas where the wildlife had almost no contact with hunters. Furthermore, in British Columbia, we have not acted on the important task of putting most of these roads out of operation once they have served their original purpose. Thus hunters, now equipped with a variety of off-road vehicles, have been able to pursue moose, caribou, elk, mountain sheep, mountain goat and grizzly bear far into what was once hinterland. In addition, aircraft travel to remote areas has made it possible for guides and outfitters to look after far more hunters than was possible forty years ago when all back-country hunting involved horse travel or back packing.

Close to our urban areas chemical pollution has become a problem. Rivers and many seashores are contaminated with a growing assortment of chemicals arising from our industry, our transportation, and from agriculture and horticulture. DDT, PCB's, heavy metals, herbicides, carcinogens and teratogens are everyday terms familiar to all those who read or who view serious television.

102

Hundreds of thousands of automobiles travel our highways through environments occupied by birds and mammals. In British Columbia alone, the mortality of wildlife on roads probably runs into the millions of creatures annually.

These major changes in the environment and more than a century of hunting and trapping have been accompanied by changes in the abundance of many species but for only a few do we have the details. The scientific and management staff is too thin on the ground and too overburdened with immediate tasks, as well as being underfunded, to undertake the detailed long-term studies required, or to keep control of illegal acts inimical to wildlife. Our capacity for damaging habitat and its living creatures has outrun our capacity to respond. Despite this only a few species are known to have been extirpated or reduced to the level of endangerment — sea otter, yellow badger, burrowing owl and sage grouse are the best known. The last three are victims of habitat destruction. Of the larger and more obvious species black bear, elk, moose, white-tailed deer and possibly mule deer are as abundant or more so than a century ago; caribou, both species of wild sheep, mountain goats and grizzly have declined.

These are just some of the realities that wildlife managers have to accept and introduce into their conservation management programs as they strive to maintain the full range of wildlife species with which our province is richly endowed.

While technology has multiplied the problems for the conservators it has also provided them with opportunities for gaining information in greater depth, variety and reliability than was dreamed of in 1947.

Fixed-wing and helicopter aircraft are commonplace tools of the trade. Not only do they speed travel and facilitate the observation and counting of widely dispersed wildlife; they also provide the opportunity for applying novel and more sophisticated census methods and for replicating them to provide measures of predictability. Biotelemetry, the attaching of miniaturized radios to animals ranging in size from moose or grizzly to mink or quail, provides fascinating details of the lives of wild animals. They assist in census, they provide a host of details that come from being able to monitor the movement of an animal; when it dies and what killed it; the size of the range it must have in order to put together a year-round living. We can follow its migrations, its hibernation, its response to changes in temperature, wind, deep snow and similar day-to-day changes in the animal's environment.

By use of surgically implanted radios, tuned to monitor heart beat rate or changes in blood pressure, we can quantify the changes that come when an aircraft flies low overhead, a wolf pack attacks, or a man appears. These can be translated into the energy cost of disturbance — which can be critical to animals facing severe winter conditions.

103

Other techniques permit measurement of the nutritive quality of the food available during the critical winter period and permit us to identify the winter ranges that must be reserved to wildlife if these large grazing animals and their predators are to survive.

It is possible now to closely monitor the actions of predators, to determine the size of the ranges they need in different terrain, the food resources and how and when they are used, the role they play in the life equation of the several species that they kill for food, as well as the important mechanisms by which they regulate their own rates of increase.

Disease and parasites can be identified and the life histories of damaging ones can be studied to determine the potential for combatting their impact by means that are practical under field circumstances.

A major innovation has been the adaptation of computer technology to research on, and conservation of, wildlife populations. With this technology, not only is it possible to store and sort vast amounts of data quickly and to make complicated statistical calculations almost instantly, it is possible also, given adequate data, to simulate real life situations in ways that permit examination of the results of simulated experiments. One of the most important contributions of such exercises is to eliminate apparently useful approaches that emerge from the simulation as unimportant.

There are other important changes that the wildlife scientist/conservator must be concerned with. Forty years ago, they were appointed to a department of "Fish and Game" — today they serve in the Wildlife Branch or in regional offices of the Ministry of Environment and Parks. In the area of birds and mammals, the difference implicit in title change is profound. In the earlier years, focus was concentrated on the huntable species, large ungulates, large predators, furbearers, ducks, geese and the grouse, pheasants, quail and partridge and in protecting them from overkill.

Today, by mandate, all resident wildlife comes into the responsibility of these biologists though some have not fully grasped this. The broadening of their biological horizons has also greatly expanded their client groups. The number of British Columbians who watch birds and animals as a hobby greatly exceeds those who are interested in hunting them with bow or firearms. So far the hunter, by paying licence fees and other taxes related to the privilege of hunting, contributes heavily to the protection of wildlife and the acquisition and enhancement of habitat. The hobby users so far contribute little or no direct financial support.

Then, too, there is a growing sentiment vigorously promoted by a relatively small group of individuals who believe, on ethical or humanitarian grounds, that hunting and trapping are no longer

104

appropriate. Some of them are urbanites with more interest in the issue than the creatures. But many are knowledgeable about the birds and mammals with a strong interest in seeing all creatures living a "natural" life with all its hazards, predators, disease, starvation, winter kill, and competitive expulsion as well as its success — survival.

The biologist knows that for many creatures we have so altered the environment and the numerical mix of species and numbers that the natural state and the processes we romantically see as operating no longer can.

So the wildlife scientist attempts to follow his education and his enthusiasm. To be constantly learning more about the creatures around him, to monitor the environmental impacts of our society in so many ways. On the survival of wildlife species; to devise ways in which we can use the natural resources from which we draw livelihood, and continue to enjoy the rich experience we can gain from the living world while the creatures that fascinate us can continue indefinitely in healthy populations.

Much of what we draw from our environment has nothing to do with science. It is true that the more we understand environmental processes and the details of the lives of wild creatures the more richly we can enjoy contact with them. Nonetheless, there is a wilderness mystique that is done violence if the elk or grizzly you see is wearing a radio collar or has long plastic ribbons streaming from its ears. These may be part of essential techniques to the scientist seeking knowledge, but they are destructive of the emotional aspect of the enjoyment so many find in wild creatures living untouched in their natural environment.

Thus there are tensions inherent in the system that are part of the rapidly changing times that find a growing proportion of Canadians living urbanized lives and deriving their attitudes toward wildlife from romanticized movies and television. These are tensions to which the biologist must adapt. The next forty years will see even more changes in technology, in attitude and in mandate than the last, and the wildlife biologist's challenge will be to focus clearly on the basic objectives of maintaining that diversity of undefiled environments on which our extraordinarily rich fauna depends and to make certain that no species vanishes through the instrumentality of man.

These goals will demand not only scientific and technical skills, but social and political sensitivity and a desire to support all the ways in which British Columbians of the future will find their lives enriched by wild creatures and wild places — provided they do not threaten those creatures and places.

". . . We found there a tall and exceedingly well-dressed man, with a face so open and frank that it attracted our notice at once. We were surprised at being told that it was he who wished to guide us to the mountains . . . As a hunter, he had but one rival . . . His age was about thirty: he was six feet high, and very powerfully and gracefully moulded. The prairies had been his school; he could neither read nor write . . . His bravery was as much celebrated in the mountains as his skill in hunting . . . I have never, in the city or in the wilderness, met a better man than my true-hearted friend, Henry Chatillon."

Francis Parkman
The Oregon Trail, 1872

The myths of a new country abound with heros: mountain men, guides, Mounties, prospectors, soldiers, explorers. Few, if any, could measure up to Parkman's guide. But British Columbia had and has its share of colourful men who search the back country for game.

Probably no place in North America south of Alaska offered the challenge for guiding that could be found in B.C. It was a challenge taken up by resolute and hardy men whose existence depended on a variety of circumstances over which they had little control, not the least of these was the government.

The story of guiding, as opposed to a story about guides, is one devoted to organization and politics and promotion. In a changing and developing world, the lone guide-outfitter faced difficult times. Only through combined effort could he put together an industry that could cope with the expensive new technology and the demands for comfort of today's well-heeled foreign hunters. It is not a story about horse-trains and grizzled guides and smokey camp fires; instead it is a story of keeping businesses alive, businesses that had and still have an important role to play in the wildlife industry of British Columbia.

CHAPTER 7

The Growth of Guiding

Leo Rutledge

It was ever thus — some led and some followed — the guide and the guided...

In British Columbia, the business of providing guiding services for big game hunters is only a century old — but "guiding," the vocation of leading and showing the way into the province's unknown is woven into our very fabric from the earliest beginning of things — indeed, into the continent's very roots...

We are told that, as early as 1690, explorer Henry Kelsey and his Cree companions left York Factory to follow the track of the Assiniboines onto the western buffalo plains. Some six decades later, in 1753, Anthony Henday, another of the Hudson's Bay Company's "bold and enterprizing servants" was also to leave York Factory. Accompanied by the Cree, he travelled across country with them until they reached the great camps of the horsed Indians.

Following Anthony Henday came the great explorers and map makers, Alexander Mackenzie, 1793, Simon Fraser, 1806, and David Thompson, 1770-1857, all assisted by native guides and guidance. The instances are legion. At one point, wrote a grateful Mackenzie, "...such an escort was the most fortunate circumstances that could happen in our favour."

It will be seen then, to attain an objective, these early expedition leaders, the guide outfitters of their time, ever sought to derive the most from what was known — a formidable task when confronted with a vast world of "unknowns."

So it has been with the guide outfitters who followed those earliest travellers. They too had sought the help of the "known," enlisted the knowledge and trail professionalism that rested with the native people. Professionalism in early guide outfitting entailed the ability to bring out the best that was inherent in the two peoples, the newcomers and the indigenous — and then forging them into an efficiently functioning trail unit.

After the earliest explorers came the seekers of substance. At first in search of furs and gold they came, betimes in waves, and all needed guides, guidance and help to transport their things. Surely British Columbia was designed especially for guides and guiding. It had so much to search for, in a land so incredibly difficult to search in.

From the shores of Hudson Bay, the fur trade's canoe brigades were guided into British Columbia's heartlands (Fort St. James 1806). Long pack brigades from the upper Missouri and lower Columbia found their way into the Kootenay's gold flurries, (Wild Horse 1864), while others from Yale and Port Douglas sought the beckoning Cariboo (1860's). No place was too far, no trail too difficult, nothing impossible. Guides became packers and rivermen, while rivermen and packers became guides.

This was the corps from which British Columbia drew its early-day big game guides. Because they had been there, they knew how to get there.

In time, paddle-wheel river-craft and railways came to venture deep into British Columbia's vastness, particularly throughout its southern half. While river craft plied the Columbia, Fraser, Skeena, Stikine and Peace, indeed, nearly all of B.C.'s major rivers, railways entered the Kickinghorse in 1885, Crowsnest in 1898, and Yellow-head in 1914, the latter two Rocky Mountain Passes; and also from Squamish on the sea.

While these transportation facilities left the northern half of the province much as it had always been, they spelled the end of much long-trail packing into the southern half. On the other hand, while the distances to be travelled by pack-trains became less, tonnages to be further transported from the many railway stations and river "ports" increased. Guides and packers were as busy as ever, albeit in a modified, short-trail capacity.

In 1885 at Kickinghorse Pass — enter the Canadian Pacific Railway to British Columbia. Understandably, after having built a railway to stimulate trade and tonnage, the C.P.R. set out to sell whatever B.C. had to sell. And, obviously, after leaving the sameness of the great plains and upon entering the Rockies, the first eye-full the company's promoters encountered was the overwhelming beauty, majesty and splendour of it all. The second was the game animals, found basking 'midst the splendour, and never again would western Canada be quite the same.

A series of interesting brochures followed, classics of their genre! Still a full century before the discovery of British Columbia's "Super-naturalness," the hype now is astonishingly familiar. The hard-sell, mainly aimed at the money of the time, Europe's aristocracy and United States' wealthy, met with no small success. Swank hotels and lodges were built, Pullman train coach access was provided, the Canadian Alpine Club was born, sport hunting in B.C. was launched and, with it, so was guiding of a new sort.

After seeing the C.P.R.'s success in the Kickinghorse and upon entering the Crowsnest and Yellowhead, the other railways followed much the same pattern and, so, the internationally known guide-outfitters, Brewsters of Banff, and Hargreaves of Mount Robson, came to be.

Let me digress here long enough to remark: fortunately for Canada and all the world, before the Rockies between Mt. Robson and Mt. Assiniboine had become hopelessly ensnarled in encumbering land alienations, the lovely necklace of national and provincial parks had been created, thanks to the few brave men and women of vision, who fought the good battle for parks.

By the end of the 1800's, in the course of the frantic search for furs, gold and all else, it had become fairly well known that British Columbia contained some outstanding big game ranges. The supply was there and so, for that matter, was the demand to bring the two together. It was just a matter of access; that's all. For the Kootenays, and the southern Chilcotin's Bridge River country, the C.P.R. solved that — as did the Stikine's paddle wheelers for the Cassiar.

This was an era when the trend-setting, sport-hunting, aristocracy of Europe and such as globe-girdling, big game hunting U.S. president, "Teddy" Roosevelt, were cutting a wide swath through North America's wild west. By the turn of the century, because their haunts could then be reached, trophy hunters had already taken scores of rams from the southern Canadian Rockies, the Chilcotin's southern extremity and from the Telegraph Creek surroundings. By then, after shooting up the U.S. west with Teddy Roosevelt, a swashbuckling Englishman, W. A. Baillie Grohman, had drifted north to do a little sniping of his own in the Kootenays: "I was fortunate enough to bag, among the seventy-eighty bighorn I got, an uncommonly fine ram, each of his horns girthing 19 inches at the base."

Also by then, in 1885, the intrepid Admiral Seymour of the British Navy had, "... stumbled across the possibility of big game in the country around Lillooet." Consequently, he and his guide, Arthur Martly, took to the hills and three weeks late returned with 15 rams. In the same general area, from 1903 to 1910, one C. A. Phair, outfitted 96 hunting parties that brought out 145 rams, along with some other odds and ends. Further, to accommodate the gold frenzy, paddle wheelers were churning the Stikine white and thus providing access to hunters. A Telegraph Creek hunter, J. R. Bradley, tells of a hunt he made in 1904 when "... our troubles and trials were numberless." For one thing, during his 53-day sojourn of the "Roosevelt Life," he encountered a lot of "moskeags." "One Indian knew more about hunting than all the rest put together because (Zoologist) Andrew J. Stone had taught him all he knows." Anyway, although he "... considered the country to be one of the hardest in the world to hunt," it was well worthwhile because, "... this is the only place in the world where Stone sheep are to be found." The largest of the hunt's six-ram take was 36 inches (horns). And all this happened at the turn of the century because of the relative ease of access.

From 1900 to 1910, the century's first decade: With southern B.C. and the Cassiar being introduced to sport hunting, someone thought there should be some rules and regulations to go with it.

In 1905, A. Bryan Williams came onto the Victoria scene to take charge of the "Game Department." Said Williams, "Even at the time of my arrival in this country, there was some sort of game laws — but they were a dead letter. No one paid the slightest attention to them."

Licenses and fees followed laws and, not only that. Williams, it seems, also turned out to be a bit of a promoter and, obviously, one with no small flair for entrepreneurship. Upon realizing British Columbia's wildlife resource was a highly saleable commodity on the global scene, the new provincial game and forest warden set forth to sell it. Accordingly, in 1910, exhibits of B.C.'s big game trophies were shown in Vienna and, later, in London and Glasgow. As may be expected, sport hunters, perhaps wearying of India and Africa, responded and the demand for guiding services followed.

At about this time, a trickle of moose appeared in British Columbia, an event that, as we shall later see, was to reveal the province's attitudes and its understanding of population and wildlife dynamics.

Until this time, however, insofar as big game's well-being is concerned, whether there were rules and regulations, or indeed, whether there was a game department at all, probably didn't really make much difference, one way or another. Access being difficult, time-consuming and costly, big game trophy hunting was only for the few and, compared with the size of the resource and its 366,255 square mile range, hunting pressure was minimal. Nevertheless, whether imminently necessary at the time or not, these well-intentioned early attempts at order in the woods no doubt foresaw times to come.

And so the ensuing decade of 1910-1920 became a milestone to remember in people-management. In 1913, for the first time, under Williams' administration, guiding was licensed in British Columbia. Although guiding had been with us for decades, if not centuries, this now recognized it as a legitimate business endeavour.

In the beginning, and indeed for the next several decades, upon presenting $5, and precious little evidence of anything else, a person could buy a license to guide anyone, for anything, anywhere in British Columbia. Thereby, a covenant of sorts, albeit tenuous, between the state and the guide, was made. However vague though they may have been, certain responsibilities were thereby assumed and delineated by both. While the state delegated responsibility, it also assumed some, as it would discover before the century had run its course. But

110

amongst all the uncertainties about who was responsbile for exactly what, some aspects emerged crystal clear:

(a) Henceforth, non-resident hunters entering British Columbia would be required to retain the services of a licensed guide.
(b) Thereby, the province was given the opportunity to capture the resource dollar value — by bid-and-offer dynamics.
(c) Henceforth, the non-resident sector of hunting in British Columbia would be elbow-to-elbow field supervised — at no cost to the province.
(d) To obtain a license, a guide must at least be thought to be qualified.
(e) From the outset, because a guide now had something to lose or gain, he had a vested interest in retaining his license. Cancel it and, as a guide, he became nothing.

Simply stated, by being licensed, the guiding industry became a highly manageable entity, not because it was comprised of particularly loveable or tractable individuals but because, to retain its license and thereby stay in business, it had to be. It can be said that the guiding industry is as disciplined as the state wills it to be.

After recovering from the trials of war and flu, the '20's were better, indeed, buoyant, for guides — until the decade's last year that is. When I left for my trap line in the fall of 1929, marten and lynx were trading at about $50 but, by spring, when I came out, they, like most things, were worth little.

A noteworthty advance in the Game Department's management of people took place in the 1920's, one that was inadvertently to have far reaching implications. Hitherto, the in-fighting among the province's trappers for territory had been bitter, and never-ending. Consequently, in 1926, to alleviate a chaotic circumstance, specific trapping territories were apportioned and allotted to individual trappers and, thenceforth, a trapper's rights of tenure, however vague they may, in fact, have been, were to be transferable to a successor or his estate.

And so, thanks to the Game Conservation Board and Frank R. Butler, its secretary, the supporting cast, and the trappers themselves, the highly successful registered trapline system came to be ushered in, the first of its kind and one later emulated throughout Canada and the United States. This benchmark in people management will be referred to later.

The "dreary" '30's: While many became impoverished and pitifully poor, some waxed wealthy and, though rather incongruous to the austerity of the setting, a trickle of non-resident sport hunting continued to enter the province through the decade.

The '40's: And again, so much of the world on fire. Again, while so many lay dead and buried, others prospered. By 1946, the big game hunting business in British Columbia never looked back. Many up-beat decades followed because sport hunting rests upon the luxury-spending of an affluent society.

The late '40's came to see British Columbia's big game hunting further stimulated, not only as there now was an abundance of hunters clamouring at the gates to hunt, but, of a sudden, there was an over-abundance to hunt for! By then, the moose trickle (1900-10), mentioned earlier, had bred itself into a torrent of voracious willow-munchers, a virtual moose pollution that was quickly chewing itself out of house and home. The up-surge of moose attracted more hunters which, in turn, caused many ranchers to look to guiding for additional income. Thus guiding has, in many cases, become a permanent, integral part of ranch operations throughout British Columbia, par-ticularly in areas of moose, deer and black bear hunting, fishing and trail-riding.

1950-60: Because of the strong demand for guiding services, the '50's saw a considerable number of additonal guides licensed to enter the business. Indeed, as had earlier happened among the trappers, so many entered that crowding soon made itself felt. The out-back's game wardens were placed in a difficult position, with no clear guidelines for granting or refusing an application for a guide's license — they were caught in a no-win situation. Consequently, the circumstance went from bad, to worse to chaotic.

Because of skimming lightly, trophy hunting in particular needs plenty of room in which to manoeuvre. Also, successful guide outfitting rests upon meticulous planning and attention to detail, often, several years in advance. Anything that disrupts plans is anathema to guiding. Plans must provide cushions to cope with such contingencies as unseasonable weather or high water.

Simply stated, because of the upsurge in business, too many guides were vying for too little room and consequently were getting in each other's way and thus interfering with the plans of one other. If an invasion of industrial endeavours upsets plans, that's one thing, but, for the guiding business to be upsetting its own affairs, that's quite another.

The story of how crowding among guides was solved is far too long to relate here. Suffice it to say the problem was resolved in much the same way as the earlier trap line dilemma had been, in some instances by the game department, other times by the guides, but more often by both. Understandably, the division was exceedingly difficult to im-plement and it succeeded only because all the players involved urgently wished it to. This, as it had earlier done for the trappers, ended the guide's inter-tribal wars over territory. It also lent some cohesiveness to guides as a group.

It follows that, because of the additional rights conferred, the guide's license became more valuable than ever — and consequently, the state's control over the industry commensurate. Business was brisk and so were the guides' efforts to accommodate the business. With a vengeance they fell to. Old Indian trails were swamped out and new ones cut. Lodges, cabins, caches, meat coolers, corrals and all sorts of things were built. Camps were improved, grazing lands were enhanced, horse herds were increased exponentially. More riggin' was accumulated. Aircraft, boats, wheels of all sorts were bought while bulldozers carved airstrips, and all because plans could now be made without one's fellow guides inadvertently, or otherwise, tearing them apart. Here was gung-ho free enterprise at its finest and the privatizing was indeed awesome to behold.

Until the day we woke up, to realize that here we were, with our lifetime experience, our total worldly gatherings, together with our bookings and carefully laid plans, all perched on the precarious pinnacle of a one-year license that could be revoked upon a whim.

Simply stated, because there were strong forces afoot that would have liked the guiding industry to go away and stay away, we felt insecure. We were apprehensive and therefore set out to obtain more security.

By now, many of us had been well exposed to British Columbia's successful registered trap line system that had been introduced some 30 years before. We understood it and knew why and how it worked. In view of our substantial equity we needed some security of tenure and, in our opinion, to make sense, that tenure, albeit at some discretion of the state, must be transferable to a successor or our estate. In other words, an arrangement similar to the well tested trap line system.

As a group, guides are loners rather than joiners. We knew nothing about organizing and even less about politics. But not forever. At least we had no preconceived strategy to encumber us, so we designed our own as we went along. Being on the bottom rung, we could only go up

Anyway, at the time, while we were jockeying for position and making our first political overtures, we were also clustering into small enclaves all over the place. Associations, we called them, which in turn succeeded in attracting Victoria's attention.

In a sense, our innumerable discussions with government and the branch became of dual-purpose usefulness. First, they stimulated interest in forging the province's many small guides' associations into one parent body that, in time, became known as the Guide-Outfitters

Association of British Columbia. Second, the formation of the provincial body added clout as we came to call it to our discussions.

The upshot was that, while the guiding industry didn't end up with tenure in perpetuity, it did make a fifteen-year deal that was transferable to a successor or an estate, which was really all we'd hoped for in the first place, and immeasurably more than the shaky, one-year stint we had before.

So at long last, after fifty years, the relationship between the state and its licensed guides that, in 1913, began as a covenant of sorts, albeit tenuous, had now become a convenant in fact. Consequently, as it stands, the guiding industry now has more to lose than ever and it follows that the more it has to lose, the less it can afford to lose it.

I shall now repeat: Simply stated, the guiding industry is a highly controllable and manageable entity, not because it is comprised of particularly loveable or tractable individuals but because, to retain its license and thereby stay in business, it has to be. It's simply a matter of "discipline or else."

Upon growing up and coming of age, what did the guiding industry see before it? Mainly a world readily accessible — and frenetically entered through the aspirations of all and sundry, a world Bryan Williams, though far-sighted, could hardly have envisioned when he licensed British Columbia's guides and hunters in 1913.

Little did Williams suspect that, within 25 years, hunters from all the world would flit in and land at places like Fort St. John, Fort Nelson, Watson Lake and Smithers in a matter of hours. Little did he then know the Alaska and Stewart-Cassiar Highways and the Dease Lake extension would soon blast the north wide open. Nor could he have foreseen the web of logging and petroleum access roads that came to accommodate such as the readily transportable outboard and jet-powered boats, snowmobiles, 6-4-3 and 2 "wheelers" — all bristling with scope-sighted arms of awesome flat trajectory.

And little did Williams think that whirling rotors would soon sink softly to earth in the forest's small glades — or that small float craft would be lake-hopping or donut-tired kites skipping from tundra to gravel-bar to alpine meadow — also, betimes, well armed.

In 1918, after Williams had acted as the British Columbia game department's mainspring for 13 years, he himself had a 10 year go at big game outfitting. Later, his writings lament, "Gone are the days of bannocks cooked in a fry pan or reflector; no longer is he (the client) content to roll up in his blankets and sleep on a bed of sweet smelling balsam boughs, with perhaps a fly to protect him from dew, rain or snow. The old fashioned sportsman is rapidly disappearing from this continent. The modern Nimrod must have spacious tents fitted with water-proof ground cloths and heated to suffocation with stuffy stoves; then there must be soft mattresses to sleep on . . . ." So one must wonder what Williams might think of today's wilderness lodges, replete with power, propane, showers and instant communication to all the world. And, indeed, the air-to-hunter, hunter-to-hunter, gadgetry of today. Heat sensors in the forest, next?

Before leaving Williams' reveries, it is interesting to note his sum-up of outfitting: "There was another man whom I took out who was somewhat trying," in fact, "quite impossible" but, "only twice had people made themselves really unpleasant and rude." He concludes: "The lot of a guide is not altogether one of unalloyed joy and pleasure. He likes it of course but the life is not one of beer and skittles."

This then, is the setting that British Columbia's guiding industry grew up in and came to know. In a few fleeting years, in this province of difficult access, everything, everywhere has become readily accessible to everyone. Nothing is remote — and little sacred. Wildlife's domain, its place to be, stands virtually undefended from the on-slaught. By the antiquated approach inherited intact from the world of Bryan Williams, it is unpoliceable. While the world whirled on, our approach to people management has stood still in time.

Yes, it is people management. Wildlife management is, in my opinion, a misnomer — a contradiction in itself. Given a place to be, wildlife can continue ably to manage itself. Life helped, managed and manipulated is no longer wildlife. It is, instead, well on its way to becoming cow-like and domesticated. The fundamental dynamics of wildlife populations have not changed — it is only the people situation that has.

In last-resort despair, while in wildlife's domain, the policing of people has looked to help from vigilantism — even to the government of Canada distributing reporting forms to the province's aspiring vigilantes. Aside from the unsavouriness of a people spying and tattling on itself, I suggest this is an unpromising approach. In advocating vigilantism, the advocators have evidently chosen to overlook that loggers, miners, petroleum people and especially farmers, the very people in the best position to observe, record and report, are extremely vulnerable to dangerous revenge and costly retaliation.

As it now stands, I suggest, despite the governments of Canada and British Columbia and the British Columbia Wildlife Federation's heroic efforts, and such measures as their, "Observe, Record and Report" programs, the policing of people in wildlife's domain is out of control — simply because, by the present approach, it is uncontrollable.

Says the B.C. Wildlife Federation's President, John Carter: "One such worry is that poaching is already rampant in British Columbia to the extent that, in some regions, one animal is poached for every one taken legally...." (Winter '87) And even back in '79 people were saying: "U.S. studies have shown that only one to five percent illegal kills are detected. Wildlife officials did the tests by leaving evidence of illegal kills in the open, such as in view of highways or on private property.

In one of the more extensive studies, less than one percent were reported.

About 100 illegal game shootings were reported last year in the region. If the percentages hold true, this means there were between 1900 and 9900 illegal kills which went undetected. The public generally speaks highly of it (wildlife regulation enforcement) until they're a part of it and then they don't want anything to do with it."

"This is the sunset rather than the dawn," — Dennis Wilders, Senior Conservation Officer, Fort St. John Symposium on North Eastern B.C. Environment, Spring '79.

Also: "Illegal killing is out of control" — Fifth Estate, Feb. '87. The supporting evidence is endless.

As it stands, the guiding industry, in my opinion, stands as an island of hope. Not because it is innately saintly but because, to endure, it has to be.

If we, as a people, determine that an animal is to be killed, then I contend the guiding industry has the most disciplined and economically rewarding means to offer, particularly for such sensitive and relatively scarce species as sheep, grizzly, goat and caribou; and where, in hunting, a high degree of discipline is essential and a reasonable economic return to the State is proper.

I contend this because:

(a) The guiding industry is highly manageable and controllable by virtue of a state issued license it cannot afford to place in jeopardy.

(b) To attain the highest possible prices for its services, the guiding industry searches the world's market. Therefore, the maximum return is captured — and virtually all of it from beyond not only British Columbia's but Canada's borders.

(c) Guided hunting is supervised hunting. The industry offers one-on-one supervision at all times — to a client willing to pay for his own supervision.

British Columbia's guiding industry has evolved into a potentially useful, wieldy and civilized means of utilizing wildlife.

Looking Ahead

The future of "guiding" in British Columbia? Frankly, I have grave misgivings...

Our fair province has all the pieces to devise the best of all possible worlds — but whether the players can properly arrange them, remains a moot point. The signs are not auspicious. In the instance of wilderness and wildlife, the guiding industry's very base of operations and stock-in-trade, we have a grave problem. Too many are saying, "Oh yes, these things and their well-being must come first of course — after me, that is.

In less than 50 years, within a brief life-span, British Columbia's resource utilization has leapt from labour-intensive benign to highly mechanized harsh. In the process, the onslaught upon wildlife and wilderness has been insensitive, relentless and unabating. Yet, despite the devastating impact of this swift transition, our attitudes and basic system of wildlife and wilderness custodianship have stood frozen in time. Indeed, it has even consistently and unabashedly pitted one wildlife user against another — and blithely stood back to watch wildlife caught in the middle! While I view the guiding industry as a potentially orderly component of the provincial tourist industry, I contend it cannot survive, surrounded by a sea of disorder. Indeed, some guiding operations, having been shunted aside, have already succumbed — and more will surely follow — as will the remainder of British Columbia's tourist industry's "Supernaturalness," if we insist upon plundering the proverbial goose before she even gets around to laying her golden clutch.

"It seemed that animals always behave in a manner showing the rightness of the philosophy entertained by the man who observes them. . . . Throughout the reign of Queen Victoria all apes were virtuous monogamists, but during the dissolute twenties their morals underwent a disastrous deterioration."

Bertrand Russell
My Philosophical Development

One of the great temptations of conservationists is to argue for the protection of an animal because of its "value" or "worth." The argument goes that this critter or that one is good for mankind because it eats mosquitoes or rats or it aerates the soil or does something that is to our advantage. This argument fails, of course, when we have to deal with an animal whose "benefits" are not yet known. Should those critters be protected as well? If not, why not?

Predators fall nicely into this perplexing situation. In the last chapter we read about the guides who opened up vast areas of the province for hunters. Some of the guides viewed predators as competition to be done away with. As one of the predator hunters said, predators do not do any good so why not kill them? Presumably his view would have changed if he could have seen, or been persuaded, that predators did indeed have a value.

Aldo Leopold, more clearly than any other conservation philosopher, said just because mankind did not understand all aspects of the biota it should not discard parts that seemed useless. To wit, the predator.

The role of predators has raged in British Columbia for decades. It goes on still, and given mankind's propensity for self destruction it will likely continue. But wildlife scientists increasingly understand the importance of a managed predator population. It seems now that it's up to citizens to understand that, as Leopold says, when you're tinkering with something you should not throw away any of the parts.

CHAPTER 8

The Predator Hunters

Lyn Hancock

Humans truly have dominion over all living things. They choose which animals will live and which die. Historically, they did it by selection (a cougar is dead, a deer is saved). Currently, they do it by destroying the habitat of living things, their own included.

Down through the ages, humans have classed some animals as "good" (their pets, their livestock, soft-eyed does and fawns), and other animals as "bad" (the slavering, red-eyed wolf, the cunning, bloodthirsty panther). An animal is "bad" if it eats a "good" animal that humans own or want, or, as somebody said, "any critter that gets something you want before you do." Before people called them predators, they called them — officially — vermin, varmints, pests, noxious animals. It is not only the physical prowess of the animal that earns humans' ire or fear or envy; it is its mythology as expressed in fable and fairytale.

So the predator must be controlled. It must be reduced in numbers or removed either by extermination or by translocation. In Europe in the Middle Ages, "bad" animals were put on trial. In North America in pioneer times, European settlers raised in the Judeo-Christian tradition and seeing themselves as separate from "nature" streamed westward across the continent, increasing their population, conquering the earth without considering stewardship, trying to tame wilderness by growing crops, raising livestock and destroying predators.

Roy Padgett, a farmer who homesteaded south of Powell River in British Columbia in the early 1900's, remembers those attitudes: "The idea was of course to raise sheep. My father was an Englishman. Vast, green rolling acres dotted with sheep; that was the dream. The whole concept of government from the Hudson's Bay Company times to quite recently was that this whole province was to be made secure for civilized man and his agriculture. I can remember, up on our own "stump" ranch, when the second-growth fir began to come up, we'd set fires to burn those seedlings with a real sense of indignation that the force of the wild just refused to admit that this was farmland now. . . . We started to get a fair flock (of sheep) built up but it was frustrating. The big thing was predators: cougars and wolves. There was no question that the wolves and the cougars did massacre our livestock . . ."

Cougar Brown, a hunter who prides himself in "killing more cougar than any man alive" is in his nineties now and lives in Port Alberni. Whereas, today, Roy Padgett wonders if predators did massacre his livestock and wonders even more whether or not he is proud of killing the predators, Cougar Brown's attitude to predators remains traditional: "I hate to kill a deer. They are such innocent-looking animals and they don't harm you unless you grab hold of one. I used to give them names: Billy and Molly and Nelly and Mary. But cougar — if it was a decent animal and worthy of feeding and wasn't harmful to the human race I wouldn't touch one of them. But they can't be trusted. They should put the bounty on them again at $100 apiece and kill the last cursed one."

The attitude of Magnus Colvin, a retired farmer from Cobble Hill, also remains entrenched: "My knowledge of cougar was gained firsthand on a stump ranch when I was a child here in 1899. When my father came here in 1883, settlers cleared a bit of land and started up on sheep, as they had done in the Shetland Islands. But the cougars started eating sheep. I remember one year in particular we started out with 40 sheep and, in the fall, we ended up with 40 sheep. All the lamb crop had been eaten up by cougar. We were holding our own, but no profit. The cougars ate the profit. . . . Cougars have no right to have dominion over man in areas where man lives."

Archie Wills, an elderly retired sports editor of a Victoria newspaper, said recently, "I never heard anybody say a good word for a cougar. They eat defenceless animals, they snarl, they're not even graceful, they're cowardly, they run, they don't defend themselves. People call them the American lion, to give them some build-up, some ferocity. You can't eat them, you can't wear them; what good are they?"

Cougars were not the only predators that people wanted and, in some cases, still want to exterminate. Wolves, coyotes, foxes, squirrels, seals, eagles, owls, hawks, falcons, crows, magpies — even mergansers and robins — were on the "bad" list and people received bounty money to kill them. Also on the "bad" list were other noxious animals, not predators in the strict sense but rodents that eat crops, like ground squirrels, prairie dogs, rabbits and hares.

Ironically, none was given the courtesy of being called wildlife. In 1912 Bryan Williams, British Columbia Provincial Game Warden, wrote under the headings, "Pests" and "Noxious Animals": "Few people actually realize how destructive to game and domestic animals these pests are. . . . It is one of the laws of nature that, as wild life increases in quantity, so also will animals and birds of prey. It is therefore necessary that these pests be destroyed or they will kill the increase of game, which might otherwise be used by men." He goes on to list the number of predators killed for bounty during the year 1910-11: 581 wolves, 277 cougars, 3,653 coyotes, 2,285 big-horned owls, and 73 golden eagles. "In two years a total of 2,896 wolves and cougar and 5,141 coyotes were destroyed, as well as a number of others poisoned and not recovered for the bounty. Allowing fifty head to each wolf and cougar and ten to each coyote, by their bounties alone 196,210 head of game and domestic animals were saved. Is it any wonder that deer are increasing almost everywhere?... During the past two years, bounties have been paid on 3,139 big-horned owls, and on the Lower Mainland they are again scarce. Is it any wonder that grouse are again increasing?"

Simple arithmetic, convoluted logic. In reading the official records of the British Columbia Provincial Game Warden from 1905 onwards — their florid exaggerated prose style, their simplistic thinking, their self-congratulatory tone — one can't help feeling that the early settlers and game wardens thought themselves engaged in a patriotic or holy war. Bryan Williams in 1914 exhorted everybody to "consider it his duty to do away with as much vermin as possible."

And not only in British Columbia. It was the same all across the continent. In 1917, Dr. Nelson, Chief of the United States Bureau of Biological Survey, proudly proclaimed his department's success in destroying the hated predator: "Everyone is aware that mountain lions, wolves and other beasts of prey destroy vast numbers of game animals. For this reason the destruction of predatory animals, while primarily to protect livestock, at the same time is helping increase the amount of game."

Even naturalists and conservationists such as Dr. William Hornaday wrote in 1914, "The mountain lion of the west, known to us as the panther or cougar, is a destructive, dangerous and intolerable pest. . . . It must be hunted down and destroyed regardless of cost. . . . We consider firearms, dogs, traps and strychnine thoroughly legitimate measures of destruction. For such animals no half-way measures will suffice."

Such measures were varied. Paying bounty has long been a custom. The exact date in history when a reward was first paid for the destruction of predators has been lost in the passing of time. But it probably goes back to the ancient Greeks, about the year 600 B.C., a period of almost 2,600 years. In the late 1500's, the Jesuit priests of Lower California paid Indians one bull for every puma killed. By 1630, the colonial government of Massachusetts was paying bounties to kill wolves. Bounty acts of both local and state governments spread quickly westward throughout the eighteenth and nineteenth centuries to include any animal thought to harm livestock, game or crops. Ranching and sporting interests, even newspapers, followed governments in providing funds for bounties and payments mounted in the early 1900's until, in the 1940's and 1950's, people received as much as $40 for killing a wolf, $50 for killing a panther. In Canada the federal government paid bounties on seals and shot basking sharks and killer whales to protect salmon.

In North America, the earliest hunts organized by settlers to kill predators were panther drives, which resembled the Inca ring hunts of South America several centuries before. Panther drives were held in Pennsylvania until 1849. The settlers killed more than panthers. In one drive organized by Black Jack Schwartz in 1760, it was reported that 200 settlers covered a circle of 30 miles in diameter to kill panthers, wolves, foxes, mountain cats, black bears, white bears, elk, deer, buffaloes, fishers, otters, gluttons, beavers and upwards of 500 smaller animals.

To control predators, people have used bows and arrows, shotguns and cyanide guns (coyote getters), spring-loaded sodium cyanide ejector mechanisms (M-44); snares, including those baited with cat-nip oil and cougar gall; killing traps and live traps, and poisons such as thallium sulfate, strychnine, and sodium monofluoroacetate (Compound 1080; called that because it was the 1080th poison tried by the Experimental Division of the United States Fish and Wildlife Branch). People have followed predators on foot, hunted them at the dens, sprayed poison indiscriminately over their living areas as well as in baits, gunned them from the air and, latterly in some cases, moved them away from their selected territories.

And who tried to control predators?

At first anybody and everybody. The old bounty hunters were a distinctive breed. They were heroes in their day, going into the dark woods to rid them of vermin, saving stock, deer and children. Hunters of cougar were probably the most colourful characters, especially on Vancouver Island, where they competed with each other to see who could kill the most. Cougar Brown, Cougar Charlie Caldwell, Cougar Cecil Smith and Bring'em Back Cougar Holcombe were some of the most legendary.

Many supported their families through the Great Depression of the 1930's by hunting predators for bounty. Fred Olsen, a hunter and logger from Lake Cowichan, said recently: "Cougars meant money then. But we thought we were doing good, too, ridding the country of vermin, taking away an animal that had been depleting our deer herds."

Dick Clarke, a retired farmer from Hilliers, hunted cougars for bounty, though he feels a bit defensive about it now: "I hunted cougars for a meal ticket when the bounty was on. I started when I was a school kid to pay for board. You have to live, don't you? I don't have the foggiest idea how many I killed. I know I got up to 15 a month and I hunted from possibly the twenties and then to when the bounty came off. The game warden wanted them killed and the public wanted them killed."

Cougar Brown has spent his life hunting and trapping predators but he is unrepentant: "I lived good on the bounty. I used to feed 15 hounds, drive a car and a truck. I had cabins all around these mountains. I built two houses in Cowichan Lake, paid cash for them, and all on the bounty. There's not a man in B.C. who's killed as many cougars as I have. Thousands. I gotta picture of me with three big cougars standing over them with a hammer. I had a gun all right but the picture was of me killing them with a hammer. I killed my first cougar when I was 13 years old and I didn't let the daylight or the dark stop me. Bald eagles, too. I used to get as much as $35 a day for just taking the head. Those eagles were great destroyers. Fly down on a bunch of grouse and eat them all up. Fly down and kill even a yearling deer, pick the eyes out of little fawns, and pack the fish out of the sea, eagles did."

Aubrey "Skate" Hames, now retired and living in Campbell River, was a logger, a hunter and trapper, later a government predatory animal hunter and a conservation officer: "I bought my first hound in 1928. It was a redtick and I paid $25 for it. I hounded coons for the pelts and sold coon skins to the Hudson's Bay Company for $8.50, each on the average. That was more attractive than working as a logger. Wages then were $4.50 a day. Then the Depression hit the coon market and they decreased in value to about a dollar and a quarter so I turned to cougar hunting."

The general pattern for controlling predators was similar across North America. At first, from the days of earliest settlement until variously the 1950's, the 1960's and 1970's, depending on the jurisdiction (the cougar is still legally bountiable in Texas), it was indiscriminate. Farmers destroyed them for threatening their crops or livestock. Hunters and trappers destroyed them for their pelts. Bounty hunters destroyed them for payment. From then until the present, under the influence of scientific management, which began in the United States, governments have gradually phased out the bounty, employed government predatory animal hunters to do the job more efficiently and selectively, made poisoning more restrictive as regards target species and methods, and designated the predator with fur and game status where instead of the government paying people money to destroy the predator, the people pay the government royalties or licence fees for the privilege of doing so. Gradually, through the 1960's, 1970's and 1980's, most political units have steadily increased the restrictiveness of their hunting regulations, protecting predators with bag limits, advertised seasons and hunting method controls. At the same time, state, provincial and federal governments have varying policies and programs to control individual predators adversely affecting crop and livestock interests. There are still provisions for destroying predators en masse if they are believed to be threatening

123

wild game populations. The ancient attitude of killing "bad" animals for the sake of "good" animals is still with us but now wildlife managers learn something of the predator/prey relationship before they do it and they no longer wish to exterminate the predator as a species.

How did this come about in British Columbia?

Bounties were introduced in the 1800's but official records began in 1905. Coyotes were bountied between 1905 and 1954, cougars between 1906 and 1957 and wolves between 1906 and 1955. (Black bears and grizzly bears were not considered vermin in the same way as cougars, coyotes and wolves, although black bears often caused — and still do — more damage to farmers and ranchers. Individual bears were destroyed after depredation, but the species was controlled by hunting regulations.)

In the first half of this century the British Columbia Provincial Game Warden congratulated himself annually on the positive effects of the bounty. "When the amount of game one of these animals kills in a year and its value to the country are taken into consideration, it must be admitted that even if a few thousand dollars have to be expended every year in their extermination, the money is well invested," wrote the Game Warden in 1906. "Thousands of birds and animals have been saved from destruction by increased bounty on such pests as wolves and cougars," he said in 1911.

The battle against the bounty was a long one. The annual records of both provincial and federal governments indicated increasingly that it was ineffective. The first hint was in 1918 when the Dominion Advisory Board on Wildlife Protection in Canada (a federal body) stated that, "The bounty system will not succeed in any territory of predatory animals." In 1925, opinions were expressed in the British Columbia Game Commission Annual Report that the bounty was a failure and that it would be less costly and more efficient to exterminate predators such as cougars by paying local hunters to shoot them in areas such as Vancouver Island where they were perceived as a special menace. In the 1929 report, the bounty was called "a costly contentious issue . . . of no lasting benefit" and caused "great fraud." Commissioner Frank Butler told the 1947 Annual Game Convention that, after spending $800,000, there were just as many predatory animals in British Columbia as when the first bounty payments were made.

According to Al West, Supervisor of Predator Control for British Columbia during the 1950's, bounties did not encourage hunting of individual livestock and game killers and did not control predators where or when it was most needed (as in difficult terrain, on summer stock ranges or during a rabies outbreak). Bounties wasted government money when it was paid for animals killed accidentally or

124

incidentally. The system invited fraud. Money was paid for boot-legged animals killed outside the paying area; e.g., Washington State or Yukon; counterfeit pelts or portions of pelts such as "ears" cut from the belly of a bobcat, "noses" from paws, or carcasses from the garbage dump were presented for payment; female predators were released in order to maintain a breeding stock to ensure future harvest and future payments; predators were destroyed and money paid in areas where it was seen that there was no need for control, as in the remote wilderness northern part of the province.

Phil Eastman, executive member of the Fish, Game and Forest Protective Association in British Columbia's Interior Zone, explained his opposition to higher bounty payments in an address to the province's first annual game convention in 1947: "The payment of bounties has never resolved this problem (reducing predators in the area where they are doing most damage) and has never resulted in any great good to the districts in which the average sportsmen does his hunting. We can tell from our statistics that the moment we raise the bounties to a high level, it is just like an atmospheric condition. When you have a low pressure area, the wind rushes in immediately and you have a storm. We realize the moment we raise these bounties to a high level, all of the pelts from all of the surrounding areas will immediately be funnelled in for payment. I daresay you can go to the traplines in the Yukon or even, perhaps, in Alberta and in Alaska and find lots of trappers' cabins that are probably packed full of predator pelts, waiting for the time to come when they will be worth more money. I do know that some of the Hudson's Bay Company and some of the large buyers, when fur pelts are low, will buy and store them for years till the market rises when they can sell them at a profit — why not the trappers and the guides and the predator hunters of the far north who must kill a lot of these animals in the course of their ordinary pursuits? So I can't see why a high bounty system is going to do any good unless we can localize these areas we have the trouble over and over which we are mostly concerned."

On the other hand, supporters of the bounty and ever higher bounties were vociferous in their opposition. Some pulled out all stops in their efforts to retain the bounty system. One argument used in 1935 was that "The continual loss of our game will, in time, have a demoralizing effect on business in general as, when people find hunting poor, merchants are bound to suffer." Others invented stories. A letter from a big game guide, presented to the 1949 Annual Game Convention, stated that "Four head of cattle were lost on the range here last summer to wolves, though the bodies have never been found."

Meanwhile, the bounty controversy raged on against a background of slowly improving attitudes to predators. Some predators seemed not so "bad" as others. R.M. Robertson, a sub-inspector for "C" Game Division, reported to the Game Commission in 1935, "In the killing of the bald and the golden eagle I am not in agreement. It is true, they do a certain amount of damage to game, but their aesthetic value and their beauty of flight is a sight worth guarding and watching. I do not consider these so-called destroyers of game in a class with the cougar, coyote or horned owl."

Hames killed a lot of cougars and earned a lot of bounty money but, in looking back now, says, "The bounty was absolutely stupid. It is a horrible thing to put a bounty on an animal like a cougar and I'm glad that people are taking another look at it. People keep saying they must be cowards to let little dogs chase them up a tree. But they have the fear and motivation for survival that every animal has; same as us. The cougar's no coward. It should be preserved."

From the 1930's to the 1960's, the most influential people in persuading the general public and wildlife administrators to conserve all forms of wildlife were the budding ecologists. Not all were scientists. Few at first were government wildlife workers, but all espoused a logical scientific view of management.

Aldo Leopold, a forester, was one of the first of those ecologists. He said, "You cannot love game and hate predators." He saw nature as an intricate web of interdependent parts, a myriad of cogs and wheels, each essential to the healthy operation of the whole. In 1933, he was appointed Professor of Game Management at the University of Wisconsin, the first such academic post in the United States, and, for the next several decades, his teachings influenced other biologists in their studies of predator/prey relations. People like Adolph Murie, studying coyotes in Yellowstone National Park and wolves in Mt. McKinley National Park; Paul Errington, studying hawk and owl predation on bobwhite quail in Wisconsin and mink predation upon muskrat in Iowa; Durward Allen, studying wolves and moose in Isle Royale in Michigan; C. H. D. Clarke, studying predation generally in the Rocky Mountain Parks of British Columbia and Alberta; James Hatter, studying moose and wolf predation in central British Columbia.

Contrary to what everyone had long thought and what sportsmen and ranchers continued to assert, the gradual accumulation of scientific evidence on predation from the 1930's, onwards, demonstrated that it was possible in some situations to produce a game crop and have plenty of predators around at the same time. In fact, predators could be beneficial to prey populations. Slowly, government wildlife administrators, first in the United States and then in Canada, first federally and then provincially, applied such scientific knowledge to wildlife management with the result that predators benefited.

Dr. Ian McTaggart-Cowan was directly responsible for improving attitudes to predators in British Columbia. In 1935, he graduated from the University of California at Berkeley. "I came back to B.C. thoroughly imbued with the role of science in the management of wildlife populations," he said. Between 1943 and 1946 he studied predator/prey relationships in five Rocky Mountain national parks. "A Bill Fisher from a Calgary Fish and Game Club, writing in the Rod and Gun Magazine, complained that the national parks were a breeding ground for cougars and wolves and that they should not be protected there. This led to my study," Cowan explained.

In 1941, as an assistant professor at the University of British Columbia, Dr. Cowan taught the first course in Canada in the biology and management of wildlife and, during the next several decades, as an official advisor to government departments, persuaded wildlife workers to have a more positive attitude to predators. It was one of Dr. Cowan's students, Maurice Hornocker, who in Idaho in the 1960's conducted the first scientific study of the cougar.

Although British Columbia was one of the last jurisdictions to lift the bounty on the wolf, it was the first to remove it for the cougar. Soon after joining the University of British Columbia, Dr. Cowan became an advisor on wildlife matters to the British Columbia Game Commission. His methods to influence predator policy were two-fold: he tried to persuade wildlife administrators (at this time non-scientific civil servants) that the bounty was ineffective as a means of controlling predators; and at the same time he tried to sensitize the public attitude to the needed change. "The latter required innumerable lectures, radio talks, meetings of sportsmen, natural history societies, church and service clubs. . . . My main themes were 1) Predator control is justified only when it is clearly evident that reducing predator numbers will lead to changes in the prey species in directions one has predetermined to be necessary (i.e., in the case of the cougar to produce more deer and livestock). The control should then be of a type which can be directed at the specific complaint individual in the precise area where the problem exists. 2) The bounty could not conform to this second requirement and furthermore 3) It was fraught with dishonesty."

The influence of biologists on government administrators, especially in predator policy, became more pronounced when a student of Dr. Cowan, W. Winston "Bill" Mair, was hired by the B.C. Game Commission in 1949 as Supervisor of the newly formed Predator Control Branch. At that time the public was divided in its attitude to predators. Most wanted all predators killed; some wanted no predators killed and others, such as the biologists, wanted to kill predators only after research of the local situation and if there was a need.

The new policy aimed to control completely (destroy) predators in agricultural and built-up areas; to vary control in game areas from "practically 100% to practically none at all," depending on the status of the prey population and how much it was controlled by hunting; and to control predators least in remote wilderness areas, depending again on the status of the prey population and the needs of local trappers, who were encouraged to control their own predators.

Traditional methods of control — trapping, snaring, shooting, chasing cougars with dogs, poison — would continue but they would have to suit the individual situation. The coyote-getter or cyanide gun used successfully by the Predator and Rodent Control Division of the United States Fish and Wildlife Service was to be used more widely in British Columbia. Poisons, particularly the much favoured 1080, were to be distributed by aircraft because of the province's tough terrain and the handful of predatory animal hunters (eight) to do it. Although none of the biologists was a champion of the bounty, it would continue until the new policies were found to be working.

Not all government wildlife workers believed the scientific reasons for discontinuing the bounty but the financial disadvantages were persuasive, as Mair explained to the 1950 Annual Game Convention: "Last year we received 1,180 wolves, 524 cougars, and 6,847 coyotes for a fine total of just over $70,000 in bounties. These figures alone are sufficient to condemn the bounty system... when you consider the $137,000 that we were given for predator control this fiscal year. Whether it is financially possible to put into effect an adequate control system while stumbling under such a bounty load is problematical."

Much depended on the men hired to carry it out. Mair continued, "The lessons learned in other countries have taught us the need for employment of men who are not only skilled in the manual details of their work, but who are pliable and searching in their thinking, so that they will see and recognize in advance the need for changes in controls and will be able to carry on research along proper lines. For, in predator control, as in all other wildlife fields, one faces constantly changing, living problems." He asked for predatory animal hunters who could put up with "hours of tedious observation and effort under the most arduous conditions... stay out in the open over one or several nights... and, I might say, that while we will not always put our dogs out in certain weather, our men must and will go out under any condition of weather."

Predatory animal hunters to help game wardens destroy cougars had been hired as early as 1920. The exploits of Adam Monks, Charlie Shuttleworth, Cece Smith and Jimmy Dewar were legendary. One friend of Adam Monks recalls him taking off after his dogs in the middle of winter, "ploughing through snow up to his armpits, not even a raisin on him, climbing up those steep bluffs just like the

128

cougars he was after, and not returning for days afterwards." Names of full-time government hunters like Adam Monks, Charlie Shuttleworth, Jimmy Dewar, and Cece Smith were already legendary. But now a staff of trained men was established to be dispatched to any area in the province where special attention to predator problems was needed. The first team of professional hunters consisted of Jimmy Dewar, "Skate" Hames, "Mort" Mortensen, Gordon Haskell, Martin Morigeau, and Ernie Samann. In 1947, financed by the Game Commission, Dewar bought trained dogs, built kennels and set up a school on Vancouver Island for predatory animal hunters.

In addition, a Bonus Cougar Hunter System was introduced in 1952, whereby cougar hunters in each major complaint area were registered and received an extra $20 for each cougar killed. They had to agree to answer complaints within specified areas and so cut down time and expense in getting full-time government hunters there. The government also hoped that system would reduce the public clamour for higher bounties.

It didn't. It seemed the more biologists worked to have the bounty removed, the more they were criticized. The controversy raged for years, both within and without the Game Commission. Sportsmen, farmers and ranchers were particularly vocal. Leo Wincowski in 1953 wrote in the popular magazine *Rod and Gun*, "It's nothing short of insulting to an experienced outdoorsman's intelligence to find the so-called wildlife experts arguing against bounties while at the same time trying to tell us that the answer to better game conditions rests with the employment of more biologists... (They) are glorified fakers who are trying to pawn themselves off on the public as 'scientists' and 'wildlife experts.' I have yet to meet one who impressed me as knowing anything more about wildlife habits than what they learned out of textbooks, all of which appears to have been a distortion of the true facts." A farmer, A. E. T. Evans, spoke for the sheep breeders in a letter to the editor of the Vancouver *Province* in 1959 when he asserted, "There's no place for the cougar in the whole province." Major Allen Brooks, a famous artist and ornithologist, spoke for some naturalists when he wrote a piece entitled, "The Predator Must Go."

Finally, bounties were removed: from the coyote in 1954, from the wolf in 1955 and from the cougar in 1957.

Meanwhile, other methods of control continued and poisoning of predators increased in areas where livestock was raised and game animals were heavily hunted. West, Supervisor of Predator Control after Mair, praised the use of poisons before the 1953 Annual Game Convention: "No improvement in the predator situation was realized until 1950, when mass destruction was begun by the use of poisons and various other devices." As an example, in 1958, "every wild-sheep range in the province" was baited with poison to protect the sheep from "outside elements" such as predators. Such a program was rated "highly successful."

West was satisfied that the new policies were working. "In some instances our control has aided various species of game . . . deer, big-horn sheep, moose in some areas and probably caribou. We have reason to believe that game birds have benefited to some degree. We know that in areas of former heavy infestations of predators, domestic stock has had benefits from the control of predators, so it is reasonably safe to assume that wildlife is in the same category," he stated.

The decades of the sixties and seventies saw increasingly sympathetic attitudes to predators. Predators were seen as only one factor in game declines or domestic stock harassment. West illustrated the others when he quoted Dr. W. C. Lowdermilk, assistant chief of the U.S. Soil Conservation Service: "This is the eleventh commandment: Thou shalt inherit the earth as a faithful steward conserving its resources and productivity from generation to generation. Thou shalt safeguard thy fields from soil erosion, thy living waters from drying up, thy forests from desolation, and protect thy hills from overgrazing by thy herds, that thy descendants may have abundance forever. If any shall fail in this stewardship of the land thy fruitful fields shall become sterile stony ground and wasting gullies, and thy descendants shall decrease and live in poverty or perish from off the face of the earth."

So now, habitat not predator control had become the buzzword of wildlife management. There were other indications of this increasingly ecological view. Game wardens were renamed conservation officers. Predator animal hunters became "animal control," then "wildlife control" officers. The British Columbia Game Commission became the Fish and Game Branch in the Department of Recreation and Conservation in 1957, with Dr. James Hatter, a biologist with extensive predator/prey experience, becoming Director in 1962.

Poisoning in wilderness areas ceased in 1961, though baiting continued in areas where livestock was raised. In 1963, the Predator Control Branch was disbanded, though predator control in response to direct complaints continued at the regional level. The first Predator Management Advisory Committee (representing farmers, ranchers, sportsmen, naturalists and the general public) was established in 1968 to advise and assist the government in the administration of its predator management policy. More were established around the province in 1974. Attention-getting predators like cougars, coyotes and wolves were not longer called "pests," "vermin" or "noxious wildlife"; they were classified first as "predatory animals" and then "game" and have now joined the lists of "good" animals (the cougar and wolf in 1966, the coyote in 1971). Later, wolves and coyotes were given furbearer status, demanding royalties. In 1979, poisons were outlawed, though they could still be used in specific and limited situations upon permit from the newly formed Pesticide Control Branch if predator damage was confirmed. Research into the biology of wildlife and public attitudes to it proliferated. In 1980, preliminary management plans based on available research were written for each species, each to be managed as an integral part of the wild ecosystem, each allowed to fluctuate naturally unless individuals (or packs) become perceived problems.

Government wildlife workers now limit their use of the word "predator." They are more likely to use "problem wildlife" instead. A problem animal can be an individual of any wildlife species which poses a hazard to human health or safety, or which damages or threatens to damage property of personal or commercial value. No longer does "control" mean exterminate. It can still be killing, trapping or poisoning but, if possible, wildlife control officers will capture the problem animal alive and relocate it. They will try to remove the actual animal causing the complaint and prevent harm to non-target individuals. They will use poison only if other methods are considered ineffective or financially prohibitive. They will not control wildlife for domestic complaints if the rancher or farmer is negligent in his husbandry practices.

The Supervisor of Predator Control is now the Carnivore/Problem Wildlife Specialist, with wildlife control officers, district conservation officers and regional wildlife biologists around the province to assist in dealing with situations where humans and wildlife conflict. In earlier days, the game warden or predatory animal hunter would jot some notes down in his diary at the end of a day on the trail. Now he fills in figures on Problem Wildlife Complaint Forms in his computerized office.

The word "predator" is still with us, but its use is restricted more to bears, cougars, wolves, coyotes and any other species of native carnivore or raptorial bird which on occasion may kill, maul or harass livestock or other domestic animals. Policies are more tolerant for some species than others: grizzly bears, cougars or any threatened or endangered species may not be destroyed by agency staff except where human safety is threatened or where the animal can be harvested under hunting regulations.

Although wildlife control officers still handle most of the complaints, in certain situations anybody can become a hunter. A farmer or rancher may destroy a predator if he has a permit and uses it at the site of a confirmed livestock kill or mauling. A manager or worker on a recognized community pasture (leased Crown land) may, under permit, shoot problem black bears and shoot or trap wolves and coyotes if they are proved responsible for chronic damage. Local trappers and hunters may, under permit, kill problem black bears, coyotes and wolves beyond bag limits and out of season in chronic problem areas. All can destroy predators if they are found to threaten human life but the animals destroyed remain the property of the Crown. Public control is allowed where man-made changes in the environment have caused unusually high concentration of predators.

Certain control methods are more permissible than others. Problem cougars and grizzly bears will be transplanted rather than destroyed although, recently, translocation is used less frequently as a result of the difficulty in doing it. Often, the wildlife control officer is not in a suitable position to tranquilize or live-trap the animal and, if he is, often he has no place elsewhere to put it. Shooting or trapping is more likely to be used than poisoning. And only government wildlife workers are allowed (by permit) to shoot problem predators from an aircraft or other vehicle.

Some people say the pendulum has swung too far in favouring predators. In 1976, when a child of seven was killed by a cougar in British Columbia, a woman from Ontario claimed it was entirely unnecessary to kill the cougar at all. She found excuses for the predator: "Is it not possible that the child teased the animal? Perhaps the cougar had babies? Why can't the animals — all of them — be left alone?"

Magnus Colvin, who does not want a cougar anywhere on Vancouver Island, suggests a solution that is an intriguing combination of the old and the new. "The game department have got an army of men running up and down the whole country. They could surround the cougar and take them away to the Rockies in a chopper."

Whereas, the predatory animal hunter was once a hero, now, because of increased public sympathy for predators being highly publicized in the news media, he may be seen as a villain.

Dan Lay, former animal control officer, is sensitive to such public criticism. He admits that, "People phone you up and give you a bad time. They print signs on my truck that I'm a freak and a sadist. They tell me I should know better than to kill poor animals."

Dan's father, Jack, also a former animal control officer, predicts that the conservation trend has passed its peak. "People have got sick and tired of hearing programs like Disney where all that predators kill is time. I bet you within the next few years, it will be just the same as it was in the fifties and people will get tired of having their ice boxes torn up by bears and having their domestic animals killed by coyotes."

Times are, indeed, changing. Despite the recent surge of sympathy for predators, wildlife managers are increasingly using predator control as a tool in wildlife management and increasingly returning to some of the most traditional control methods. The result is heated controversy.

During the last decade, populations of ungulates (hoofed animals such as elk, mountain sheep, deer, moose and caribou) have been declining "overwhelmingly" in northeastern British Columbia and deer have been declining "drastically" on Vancouver Island. At the same time, wolves have been increasing "phenomenally" in both areas so that they now support probably the highest densities of wolves in North America.

When hunters, trappers, farmers and ranchers reported these increases, accused wolves of "killing off all the game" and called for predator controls such as poison and local extermination, government biologists were loath to believe such empirical observations and politicians feared a public backlash if they did what the observers suggested. It was several years before regional biologists, John Elliott in the north and Doug Janz in the south, were permitted by the politicians to begin scientific experiments to prove the problem and affirm the solution. Eventually, they set up controlled outdoor laboratories in which wolves were destroyed in one area but allowed to function naturally in another. They aimed to determine whether or not, indeed, wolf predation was the major factor causing the dramatic decline in the prey species.

Factors such as severe winters, depleted habitat and hunting pressure by humans can trigger initial declines but, once the prey fall to below a certain critical level (the so-called predator pit), wolf predation alone is capable of maintaining the downward slide. The particular problem in these two areas in British Columbia was that wolves were found to be killing so many young ungulates that not enough of them were reaching breeding age (being recruited) to sustain the prey species' overall numbers. As the wolf population increased, so the ungulate population decreased — alarmingly so for the hunters of the province.

Starting in 1978, biologists in northeastern British Columbia began experimenting to test the effectiveness of wolf control as a means of increasing caribou in the Horseranch and Level Mountain areas, moose and mountain sheep in the Kechika Valley, and mountain sheep, elk, caribou and moose in the Muskwa Valley. They monitored ungulate populations in areas in which up to 80% of the wolves were killed (by shotgunning from helicopters) and other areas in which none was killed.

The results of such predator control were dramatic. In the Horseranch and Level Mountain study areas, where wolves were removed, the recruitment of caribou calves into the population increased to 16-

17%; in the Kechika, moose calf survival increased tenfold and mountain sheep lambs twofold. In the Muskwa, moose responded to wolf control with four times as many calves per 100 cows, elk with three times as many calves, and mountain sheep with twice as many lambs and three times as many yearlings. Caribou continued to show good recruitment. When wolf control terminated for World Expo Year, 1986, juvenile survival dropped dramatically again.

Similar results were achieved on Vancouver Island, where wolves were destroyed in the Nimpkish Valley and radio-collared for movement study in the Adam River watershed. In contrast to aerial shooting by one government wildlife worker, which is the control method in the more open spaces of northeastern British Columbia, wolves in the forested and logged areas of Vancouver Island were trapped first, then shot — by hunters, trappers and the general public as well as members of the Ministry. Unfortunately for controlled wildlife management, some individuals took matters into their own hands to kill wolves, a return to traditional habits, and scattered indiscriminately strychnine- and cyanide-laced baits, even dishes of anti-freeze.

The government's present policy is to reduce wolves in selected areas on Vancouver Island. Statistics affirm that reports of wolf problems in populated areas are declining and that, where wolves have been reduced, deer populations are seeing their first increases in fawn recruitment in many years.

So far has the public attitude to predators changed in the past half-century, indeed in the past thirty years, that the highly publicized killing of wolves in northeastern British Columbia shocked an impressive proportion of the human population, especially in urban areas, away from the action. Biologist Elliott was even labelled in the press as the Clifford Olsen (a mass murderer) of wildlife management. Paul Watson, leader of the Sea Shepherd Society, a zealous conservation group, offered $2,000 for the best "trophy" shot of wolf slayer Elliott (referring to the Branch's aim of managing wildlife populations in this part of the province for hunting). On Vancouver Island, Doug Janz and the biologist in charge of the field operations, Knut Atkinson, used less obvious methods, did not attract the interest of the media and animal rights groups in the same way and thus escaped public criticism more quietly.

Older biologists, who had once turned away from predator control, are now espousing it again. Dr. James Hatter, one of the early biologists who studied predator/prey relationships in the 1940's during the beginnings of scientific management, was "skeptical of the need for wolf control then ... but I was wrong in a way. I was looking at abundant moose populations, less hunting pressure and less harmful human damage to habitat. I didn't know then about the predator pit. I used to think wolves just took the surplus of the prey population. But we're not in balance any more. On Vancouver Island there are only patches of mature timber left for the deer's winter protection. There are many more roads for easier access to the prey by both wolves and human hunters. In looking at the situation now, I see that we should not have encouraged so many deer to flourish in the Nimpkish. We should have started killing wolves much earlier. In those days we went overboard on lack of predator control. We're finding now that, while generally speaking, predation is not the main factor controlling prey, it is more important than we thought."

And elsewhere as well: in Alberta, biologists found that a small herd of caribou was being eradicated. After considerable research, the scientists ruled out habitat deterioration, overhunting, poaching, bad weather or disease as controlling factors in the decline, and decided to assess wolf predation. Their announced solution of destroying wolves brought howls of protest from the two-legged kind and the project was shelved, "pending further study." In Yukon, biologists who believed grizzly bears were eating too many moose calves chose a less explosive solution by encouraging or just allowing more hunters to kill bears.

In the Cariboo area of British Columbia, in a region where the needs of ranchers and hunters must be addressed, biologist Daryll Hebert noted a lack of mature, large-curled bighorn sheep and a low recruitment rate. He found that coyotes were preying heavily on lambs and countered this by hiring a trapper to reduce the coyote population. He initiated a study and early results show that cougars, perhaps only two females and their young, have learned to prey on mature rams in the post-rutting period, when they habitually disperse to the gulleys leading down to the Fraser River. If that is so, then removal of a few cougar may benefit these bighorn sheep.

Nowadays, wildlife managers use many methods of predator control: shooting, trapping, poisoning, liberalized hunting regulations, economic reimbursement, live-trapping and translocation, habitat modification such as controlled burning or suppression of fires, mechanical barriers, repellents and biological controls. Hatter favours poison, particularly 1080, for destroying wolves "in any habitat; 1080 is the least costly, the most effective, and is highly specific to wolves. But public opinion and the kind of terrain on Vancouver Island forced us to use trapping instead." Poison as a method of predator control is still highly controversial among biologists and even more so among the general public.

Hatter believes that, "If public opinion would stay out of it, wildlife managers would manage wildlife better." That may be true but, practically speaking, the wildlife administrator must answer to the farmer who does not want to share his land or livestock with predators, to the hunter who wants meat, the hunter who wants trophies, the forester and logger who want trees and jobs, the naturalist who wants to look at the animals alive, and the general public who want just to know they are there. Emotions are just as real as the physical components of the environment, in deciding which animals live, which die. Humans still have dominion over all living things.

*"I am not one of those who think that the people are never in the wrong.
They have been so, frequently and outrageously, both in other countries
and in this. But I do say, that in all disputes between them and their rulers,
the presumption is at least upon a par in favour of the people . . . when
popular discontents have been very prevalent, it may well be affirmed and
supported, that there has been generally something found amiss in the
constitution, or in the conduct of government. The people have no interest
in disorder."*

Edmund Burke, 1770

We have just seen how "the people" as Burke calls them can be
wrong. The public's interest in predators has fluctuated wildly; their
knowledge has progressed from almost none to a little. Self interest
seems to have dictated attitudes toward predators. But generally, the
interest in wildlife going back to the earliest groups of naturalists has
been unselfish, or at least well meaning. More often than not,
however, governments have merely paid lip service to the concept of
public involvement. It is a mark of the dedication and commitment of
the wildlife support groups that they are heard as much as they are.

It is fair to say that most of the problems facing wildlife management are not technical but political. As pressure increases on the
resource and its habitat people must ask themselves if the trade-off is
really worthwhile. How much more surplus coal, for example, do we
need to produce at the expense of big horn sheep? The vexing
problem facing citizen conservation groups, whether relatively passive or radically militant, is how to plug into the system before the
decision is made rather than arriving on the scene only in time to
object.

Governments, if they are concerned about citizen involvement,
must recognize that the social mechanism to deal with these relationships is sadly lacking. We can put radio tags on moose and trace their
every move; we haven't yet found an acceptable way to determine
what "the people" really want in wildlife conservation. But you can
see in the next two essays that it is not for want to trying on the part of
"the people."

CHAPTER 9

Wildlife Societies in B.C.

Lee Straight

Few will dispute that game and fish protection, followed by total wildlife conservation, were instituted in prehistoric times on this old earth by hunters and anglers. It was for selfish reasons, certainly, and usually those sportsmen were aristocrats and other rulers. All the old, lasting parks and fish and game preserves, private though they were, and cruelly protected by death penalties in Europe and Asia, were instituted by the upper classes. It was not only for their shooting, fishing, coursing and hawking pleasure, though those were the incentives. Back even then, the aristocracy could also afford, since they ruled all, to protect flora, fauna and habitat for their viewing pleasure and, yes, with concern for their children, which is what we call posterity.

Such evolution and history will, it is hoped, be discussed elsewhere in this book. Before the history of the development of citizen conservation in British Columbia is summarized here, it is necessary to point out one great difference between the key principles behind conservation in Europe and Asia, on the one hand, and, so far, those in the New World, on the other. From the beginnings of wildlife conservation and the regulation of its use in the Old World, wildlife has been perceived as private property, always associated with the land and water that support it. Even migratory animals, such as deer or birds, were privately owned by the owner of the land upon which they were encountered. One exception is that owners of land or riparian waters did sell or rent fishing and shooting rights. But the concepts always were that the fish and game themselves are private property.

In the New World, however, with swarms of wildife surrounding the sparse aboriginal and immigrant human populations, it was immediately popular to view that wildlife as a common property, belonging to all, especially since most of the immigrants had, back "home," been unable to afford sport. From the outset, the invaders carried on the aboriginal philosophy found on all the new continents — that wildlife is the property of all.

What happened next is well known and, in fact, was an off-shoot of privately owned Old World wildlife. It is market hunting. Long before our wildlife seemed over-utilized by the burgeoning populations of invaders, market hunters were already prowling North

America's shoreline and the North Atlantic to harvest fish, sea-mammals and furbearers in swelling quantities. That's what led to the first North American national, state and provincial fish and game laws. Long before sport hunting or angling, or scientific collecting became threats, market hunting and fishing were dangerously depleting and even extinguishing varieties of fish, wildlife and plant life. The first to notice it were, of course, leisure hunters and anglers, which included some affluent farmers or ranchers. It was apparent also to trappers, who possibly were the first in the New World to practice the concept of wildlife management — trapping just enough fur on their own lines to maintain breeding stocks. Whichever came first, the progressive trapper or the far-sighted sportsman, one or other or both pressed the government and enforcers of the day to restrict wildlife harvesting and enforce some form of husbandry.

Up sprang clubs and societies dedicated to preserving huntable and sport-fishing stocks of their desired quarry. Generally later but similar to the angling and hunting groups were commercial and natural history societies, some inaugurated by egg- and skin-collectors, some by nature lovers. At the start, many non-professionals were both. In fact, most devoted hunters and anglers were and are naturalists to some degree — amateur biologists, ornithologists or botanists. Famous John James Audubon was both. It's only in the past few decades that recreationalists have specialized, generally they are more often only hunters, anti-hunters, birders (bird-watchers), and so on. Most rod and gun (fish and game) clubs of the 1920's to the 1950's contained all types of nature-lover. There were only a few natural history societies around in those days and members of those groups still were dismissed as tweedy men with spectacles, and old ladies in tennis shoes. What an unfair stigma! No wonder naturalists, conversely, seemed eager to discredit followers of the blood sports!

It took until the 1960's to sort out the true aims and impressions of devotees of Lord Nimrod and Izaak Walton from those who also followed John Burroughs, John Muir, Audubon, Henry David Thoreau and, yes, Carolus Linnaeus (Carl Von Linne), the cunning Swedish taxonomist, who devised the modern international system of classifying all organisms. That sorting out had a rougher road in British Columbia, whose people, as a group, are viewed as most independent. They also may be less seriously dedicated to flag or politics. Some say they care more for labour unions and pursue the greatest variety of team and field sports in the world. It's even possible we have a little brother or sister complex, being one of the newest provinces or states and furthest west, surpassed in that respect only by Alaska and Hawaii. Be that as it may, our citizen wildlife groups quite logically are demonstrably patterned more after United States groups than those of Europe or Asia.

140

The chronology of influences and events in the formative stages of British Columbia citizen wildlife watchdogs is elusive, fifty to even one hundred years after the clubs were formed. Some were formed to press for wildlife laws and their enforcement. Some were just fellowship clubs, even "bragging" clubs and mostly social. Most were mixtures of all, including in their titles such words as "protective" and "conservation," and their main concerns, such as "game," "wildlife," "waterfowl," "fur," "fish," "forestry," "field," "campfire," and so on. Whatever their primary or secondary aims or interests, they at first informally, through lobbying and letters to the press, then directly, by formal resolutions passed at meetings, greatly influenced their government representatives toward passing laws to protect and regulate the use of fish, wildlife, flora and habitat. It is difficult to find good records of the early influences because records of small organizations — even those that grew — were not enshrined often in any sort of archives. On the other hand, annual government reports credited most action to legislatures, parliament and congress.

There is no record in British Columbia of a province-wide organization before the formation of a group in the early 1930's labelled the British Columbia Fish and Game Protective Association. Yet many individual rod-and-gun, hunting, angling or natural history clubs, societies or associations date back to the turn of the century. Fish and game clubs in Kamloops, Kelowna, Victoria and several in Greater Vancouver were formed around 1900 and soon after — certainly before World War I. There were at least two natural history societies in the province. There were fur-breeder groups but there appears no record of organized groups of trappers, fish or game guides, outfitters, or marina operators — before World War II. There were, no doubt, tourist associations. Well established were boards of trade or chambers of commerce, but there is no record of the latter civic groups showing much interest in fish or wildlife until well after World War II, and only rarely on the conservation aspects; more often on tourist requirements and potentials.

Researching the evolution of fish and game management, we find the earliest comments on British Columbia wildlife recorded in the periodic reports of the federal government. Which brings us to one of, if not *the* earliest government agency champions of fish and wildlife in the province. He is a British immigrant, as were most of this province's influential citizens of the day. A. Bryan Williams, known as the Chief Game Warden, was quoted several times in a hard-bound document entitled "Conservation of Fish, Birds and Game," a report of a Commission of Conservation, issued after a meeting on November 1 and 2, 1915, presumably in Ottawa. In just one of many reported comments, Bryan Williams stated that, had it not been for the sportsmen who went into northern British Columbia, some of the

141

people in the smaller villages there would have had a very hard time indeed . . . the average sportsman from the United States spent $1,000 per moose (at least $10,000 in 1987 equivalents). That is the earliest record of a British Columbia wildlife director boldy acknowledging the tourist revenue values of our wildlife or fish.

There are earlier champions of wildlife conservation in writers who yarned about their travels here, usually visiting sportsmen, sometimes British doctors or government agents posted in this colony for a time. Outstanding, his book much coveted, is the much-lettered Canadian Pacific Railways surgeon, T. W. Lambert, stationed at Kamloops for twelve years at the turn of the century, whose book *Fishing in British Columbia* was published in London in 1907. Lambert, like Bryan Williams, was first and foremost an outdoor sportsman. He was a devoted and skilled angler. Some of the catches he rang up, back when every lake seemed a cornucopia, are astounding. On well known and still very productive Lac LeJeune, then appropriately called "Fish Lake," near Kamloops, Lambert ran up creels of around 100 trout per day, "cleaned, salted and packed each day by some Indians, so that none was wasted, and no fish returned to the water except the very smallest."

Hence, Lambert made bold observations about the potential attraction of British Columbia angling after it became better known. He dabbled in taxonomy in speculating on what kind of fish were those huge "silver" trout caught in fall at the mouth of the Nicola River, a Thompson River tributary. That steelhead trout run wasn't noticed (though world famous now) until reported in the *Vancouver Sun* in 1948. Lambert also speculated about another variety of silver trout, the much smaller fish of Nicola Lake, which he reported were considered by some to be a small sockeye salmon. We now know that is true. They are kokanee salmon.

Comments such as those, and from other writers such as world travelling Briton P. M. Stewart on big game hunting, and great American biologist and conservationist W. T. Hornaday, were well read by Canadian fish and game devotees and found their way into meetings and then formal recommendations to governments. Bryan Williams, a university graduate from Britain and a keen angler and hunter, exemplified such educated, enthusiastic visitors.

Williams' successors told me he was a colourful administrator. Certainly he wrote graphic books that now are classics in the literature of British Columbia hunting and angling. They are not on game administration or conservation, though Williams was reported to be acutely aware of those requirements. The books discuss where to use one's rod or firearm. British Columbia angling and hunting guide books and periodicals to this day have evolved from Williams' *Rod and Creel in British Columbia* (1919) and *Fish and Game in British Columbia*

(1935). Williams was in that respect the ideal fish and game administrator, an enthusiastic angler and hunter who appreciated the nuances of interest in those resources. His magnum opus is in the style of the books of the other globetrotting hunters of the early twentieth century, and is entitled *Game Trails in British Columbia* (1925), cherished among British Columbia hunting buffs.

The book is well-written or edited, or both, and, for the times, beautifully illustrated with photographs. It afforded most of us young, aspiring nimrods realistic escapes into big game hunting in British Columbia, or like places in the north temperate zone. It was in this book that Williams indulged in some history of game management up to his days in the province. "Even at the time of my arrival in this country (1888) there was some sort of game laws, but they were a dead letter," he wrote in the mid-twenties. "Later on," continued his report, "a more elaborate game act was passed." That first, very brief game act was passed in 1859. The next, to which Williams alludes, was greatly enlarged and passed in 1890. "But it was not until ... game was in danger of complete extermination," he wrote, "that the Government ... took any proper step toward its conservation. Then their inital move (in 1905) was to create the position of Provincial Game Warden and appoint me," modestly writes Williams, "to that office."

Williams wrote that he had a rough time, starting with no expense account or even an assistant, and that he talked the government into more financial and personnel assistance, and grew proud of his position. It is quite clear that Williams, like any other good bureaucrat, was pressing his government to perform better.

Williams reports in *Game Trails in B.C.* that he retired in 1918, after thirteen years as Provincial Game Warden. Possibly sponsored by and no doubt assisted by Legislative Member Sebastien Helmcken of Victoria, Williams left some milestones in wildlife legislation. Apparently it was at Helmcken's urging that Williams was hired. Between them they expedited the penalties for over-limit game bags and now-illegal sale of game. He and Williams instituted hunting licences for non-residents ($50, even then!) and the first budget for wildlife management ($10,000 in 1908, $18,000 in 1910). The Game Act was consolidated. Deer were liberated onto hitherto barren Queen Charlotte Islands. The first resident firearms licence appeared in 1913. Forty thousand were sold. Behind all those bold moves were the clubs, or just influential anglers and hunters, urging the members of the legislature.

Williams also reported in *Game Trails* that he was retired (laid off) because of a "rigid economy" (right after World War I) and because a new government's "views on game protection were at a decided variance with the views of their predecessors" (the outgoing government). "My position," continued Williams, "was done away with and a commission of five unpaid members appointed instead." Enforcement of the game laws was returned to the provincial police.

For ensuing history of management of fish and game in British Columbia, we are indebted to Bill Ward, the game warden who inaugurated and for years published *Wildlife Review*, still being published privately. After a World War II record that included front-line battle experience, and a stint as a reporter for the Army paper, *Maple Leaf*, Ward became a game warden in Kamloops and soon started the mimeographed information sheet, *Game Patrol*, followed by a radio progam called "Conservation Calling." The *Game Patrol* became the *Wildlife Review*. Ward transferred to the head office of the Game Commission in Vancouver (now in Victoria). He retired in 1976. His creation had grown to a circulation of 30,000 mailed to 70 countries. Ward's capping achievement is a couple of scrapbooks, one now in the provincial archives, the other still in his home. It is from his home records, kindly supplied with the aid of Ward's wife Edna, that we bridged the gap between Bryan Williams' retirement in 1918 and, in 1945, my appearance on the scene as a full-time *Vancouver Sun* outdoors writer. The Wards informed me that:

The five-person Game Conservation Board appointed in 1918 consisted of chairman, Dr. A. R. Baker, William G. McMynn, Superintendent of Provincial Police (acting as ex-officio game warden); and three unnamed members, all appointed by an order-in-council. There was persistent dissatisfaction from the game clubs with game enforcement by the provincial police, according to a note from James G. Cunningham, an ensuing commissioner, so the Game Conservation Board was disbanded in 1929. Bryan Williams was lured out of retirement to become Provincial Game Commissioner. Subsequently there was the appointment as commissioners two wildlife-minded provincial officers, Frank R. Butler, who had been secretary of the Game Conservation Board; and the aforementioned Cunningham, formerly district warden of "E" Division (Greater Vancouver). Headquarters was moved from Victoria to Vancouver. There then were 65 people on staff.

The Game Department (or Commission) again was reorganized, in 1934. Williams retired permanently and a three-man Commission of Cunningham, Butler and A. G. Bolton was inaugurated. Bolton had been chief provincial fisheries supervisor, running three trout hatcheries, one each at Stanley Park, Qualicum Beach and Sooke. Two years later Bolton retired with ill health, and the two-man Commission of Cunningham and Butler continued famously until Cunningham died of a heart attack in 1954, leaving Butler as sole arbiter and chief until he retired in July, 1962.

It was Cunningham who admitted to Ward that "game associations grew greatly in strength and influence from 1918 to 1929," and that "there was continual dissatisfaction with game administration under the police . . ." So ends our key package of history from Edna and Bill Ward, now happily retired in Victoria.

Reflecting on my own contacts from 1945 to the end of Butler's tenure, it is vividly recalled that the two commissioners were alert to public desires, suggestions and demands. They impressed most of the fish and game people, and me in particular, as cautious to the point of reluctance (being good bureaucrats), but one didn't need a two-by-four to get their attention. On the contrary, led by Cunningham as the liaison officer, they sponsored and helped guide the strong B.C. Wildlife Federation we have today. Data is hazy on this but it's almost beyond doubt that Cunningham and Butler started the first province-wide fish and game organization. They called, or agreed to call, it the "B.C. Fish and Game Protective Association." They set up zones, which Cunningham visited regularly. The zones comprised regional groups of clubs which had their own annual conventions, financed by the clubs, with assistance in the form of speakers and attendance by game wardens and the two game commissioners.

As the more erudite Butler minded the head office in Vancouver, attending only major events as the competent speaker he was, Cunningham, built like a bear, very folksy, jovial and big-hearted, roamed the hustings. Cunningham invited any and all comment about fish and wildlife management. There was no wildlife or fisheries biologist yet, though there were a few in the United States agencies. The makers of fish and game laws and mangement programs were, first, the game wardens (Conservation Officers to be), then the club members. Attendance at club meetings by the local warden, or sometimes the federal fishery officer, was a must. Wardens and sportsmen rapped with one another and formal resolutions resulted. Hence, the fish and game club members had a strong hand in formulating management programs and laws, though strongly prompted by the ostensibly wiser wardens, or occasionally, by a trapper, farmer or birdwatcher.

The arrangement wasn't original. Owners of salmon and trout fishing rights and of hunting rights in Europe operated somewhat the same way, except that in North America those rights were almost entirely common properties. It worked well in British Columbia but had two serious shortcomings. Though there were zones of clubs, there was no single, province-wide organization. (Only two provinces had one up to the late 1930's, I believe, Ontario and Alberta, though others came quickly.) The other serious shortcoming, appreciated slowly and voiced with some trepidation, is that the British Columbia meetings were sponsored by the government, through the Game Commission. So strongly benevolent was the government that not until 1957 did the clubs form their own, completely independent federation. Even now they accept, urge or demand government grants toward their annual operating budget.

That first B.C. Fish and Game Protective Association limped badly. I recall that there were "Zones of the BCFGPA only on Vancouver Island, Lower Mainland, Interior and West Kootenay." Northern B.C. and even the East Kootenay were really the "boondocks" in the 1940's. There were mutterings about the looseness of the set-up and the perceived lack of influence.

Because the role of game departments was mostly game and fish law enforcement, our departments still were under the chief law enforcement officer in those days, the Attorney-General. Perhaps it was just luck or perhaps the coalition government of 1947 heard whisperings, but it appointed as "A-G" a lawyer who was an active sportsman of every sort, especially fish and game — Gordon Wismer of Vancouver. I prefer to think that A-G Wismer had been reading the *Sun* paper and two bold little fish and game magazines, one, *Game Trails of B.C.*, first published by Claude Sissons, in January 1937; then the *Northwest Sportsman*, first published by Hal Denton and Jim Railton in 1945.

Prompted by the late J. J. "Mickey" McEwan of Nelson, a pioneer in our conservation evolution, those magazines and I, as a newspaper columnist, supported our first truly province-wide fish and game organization. It was shakier in some respects than the game commissioners' Game Protective Association, but more truly provincial. McEwan called it the "Sportsman's Clearing House."

McEwan started writing letters and articles about it in 1944, prompted by a 1939 attempt at a province-wide convention, in Kelowna, of the Fish and Game Protective Association, which was poorly supported by the coastal zones. District rivalry had then boiled up, and the Lower Mainland groups abandoned the Interior and went their own way with delegations to the Legislature in Victoria. When I appeared on the scene in November 1945, I was pounced upon by McEwen (by mail) and informed that his clearing house idea had sympathy from the *Game Trails* magazine. I printed coupons in my column, soliciting a show of interest around the province. Then the *Northwest Sportsman* magazine, provoked obviously by competion from the then better established *Game Trails*, went one better — very much better. Publisher Denton offered to run the Clearing House from, and through, his and Railton's magazine pages and office.

The Clearing House limped along, not strongly unifying the clubs, until the aforementioned Wismer, no doubt at the urging of his game commissioners, announced a province-wide game convention for May, 1947, at Harrison Hot Springs.

Those conventions, which ran for eleven years until 1957, varying their location, were good. They were at government expense, even delegates' travel costs included. Scientific presentations from northwest state and provincial agencies were included. Above all, they provided the means for the eventual organization of a truly independent, province-wide wildlife body. At the first annual game convention, Mickey McEwen gave a long paper on the need for a province-wide group, watering the seeds he had planted with his Clearing House. At the second annual convention in 1948, cautious but active and wise Phil Eastman of Revelstoke said during discussions on a province-wide group that he didn't wish it to be a "parent" group; that he wished it to be the "child" of the clubs and zones. Nevertheless, all voted to pursue the concept, however cautiously. Eastman favoured a "council of zone reps," and eventually was elected the first chairman.

At meetings in delegates' rooms, the Sportsmen's Council was formed and the ball was rolling. First Council officers were Eastman, President; Harvey Sedgewick of West Vancouver, Vice-president (and eventually president); and Bob Carswell, Vernon, Secretary-Treasurer.

In his annual address at the third game convention in 1949, Commissioner Cunningham acknowledged that the clubs had formed a federation and said little more about it. I recall the occasion and that his tone was of reluctance, especially since Cunningham had vigorously and skillfully fathered the old arrangement since his appointment fifteen years earlier. The real break came when the B.C. Fish and Game Council, properly constituted and registered under the Society Act, was set up after those sessions, separate from the regular transactions of the annual game convention. So, we had the first annual meeting of the Fish and Game Council, along with the third annual (government hosted) Game Convention.

Still, the government game conventions continued, as we said earlier, until 1957. The 1957 Convention was in Penticton and that's where the smoke hit the fan. The Fish and Game Council announced there that it was holding its own convention at its own expense the next year in Penticton. Also, a strong protest was raised there against the government's appropriation of the Conservation Fund, transferring it to consolidated (general) revenue. That fund consisted of annual surpluses from licence revenues, greater than annual wildlife budgets. The budgets now were perceived as skimpy, the management improvident. When the government took those surpluses without any of the expected public-access land purchases, the air was thick and odious in the old Hotel Prince Charles Hotel Convention room.

The first truly independent convention did not come, therefore, until 1958, a year after the name of the Fish and Game Council was changed to "B.C. Federation of Fish and Game Clubs" under the

Society Act in July 1957. The convention again was at Penticton, but without the chairman of thirteen years, the most able Commissioner Butler.

The directors who bit the bullet at those historic 1956 and 1957 meetings were: E. L. Ted Barsby of Nanaimo, Bert Palmer of Vancouver, Roland Johnson (their lawyer) of West Vancouver, J. J. McEwan of Nelson, Jim Railton of Vancouver, George Harman of Princeton, Alex Norman of Qualicum and Bill Kreller of Oliver. In 1957 Norman retired, while F. D. Marshall of Nanaimo and John Welton of Trail were elected.

Hal Denton, who had operated the Sportsman's Clearing House until the Fish and Game Council was formed in 1951, sold his partnership in the *Northwest Sportsman* magazine to Jim Railton in 1954. Railton then served as an unpaid secretary of the Council from 1954 to 1957. The magazine ceased publication in 1977. The *Game Trails* magazine ceased publication in the early 1950s.

With a few ups and downs, the Federation, which again changed its name to B.C. Wildlife Federation in June 1965, has thrived to become a 175-club, 40,000-member group with an annual budget of over 1.3 million dollars. It has hired several executive directors, four of whom have dedicated their lives as professionals, going on to other, related successes. Since all of them rose from just fish and game club members, this chapter would be incomplete without a little about them:

Howard Paish, first a teacher and school principal, was (and still is) most dynamic. He was a strong club and zone leader and, as expected when appointed the full-time, paid director, continued as more of a leader than an employee. He has gone on to become a successful environmental-recreational consultant.

Ed Meade was a senior journalist and, for a time, an outdoors columnist. After his stint as Federation executive director, Meade eventually slid quite naturally into a position with the provincial travel ministry. He died prematurely in 1972. Meade was a journeyman in all his work, whether reporting or managing and, particularly, at serving the public.

Geoff Warden also had a teaching degree but never stayed with education. He eventually moved from the Wildlife Federation into a government job, then became a consultant on fisheries and wildlife work.

Latest and most memorable executive director was Bill Otway, who served for years as a brilliant negotiator for the Federation, especially with government agencies perceived to be out of line, indifferent or otherwise remiss. Some say that Bill operated like a labour union leader but, though he could be abrasive at the height of his dudgeon, and though a large chap, he never was bullying. Mainly, he was rarely wrong, only ambitious. Otway is a master — though not formally trained — statistician, and one of the best men at thinking on his feet that I've ever seen. He resigned from the Federation over his policies as manager, mostly over money but with no charge against his honesty in handling it. He was accused of being too ambitious and brave with the Federation's promotions and campaigns, and investments in publications for sale. He later worked for a time as a travel agent, unsuccessfully ran for parliament and eventually became an ombudsman and recreational advisor on a consultant basis with the Department of Fisheries and Oceans, and now is on his third annual contract with it.

The Federation, after Otway left, changed its direction, contracting with the brilliant, veteran information officer-photographer Mike Halleran, lured away from a federal fisheries position, to produce a series of educational video programs, known as *Westland*, for the Knowledge Network on TV. On all environmental subjects, they are excellent. In rural areas that are not deluged with TV channels, the programs are particularly popular.

The nearest person to an executive director now in the Federation is executive-assistant-to-the-president, Bill Warcham, hired eighteen months ago (1986) when then-president John Carter, devoted and energetic as he was, just couldn't operate without such an assistant.

Elected president last spring is retired civil servant Stewart Reeder of Victoria.

The British Columbia Wildlife Federation almost from its inception has been the largest conservation organization in the province, just as the Canadian Wildlife Federation and the National Wildlife Federation of the U.S. are the largest in their respective countries. These grand groups are composed almost one hundred percent of what we like to call primary users of fish and wildlife — those who don't profit from their interest in, or use of it, except through personal hunting or angling; or what, for lack of a better expression, is "non-consumptive" use, a self-contradictory definition that means photographers, hikers or any other viewers, some of which latter class do belong to wildlife and angling clubs.

Natural offshoots of the big federations are specialized organizations encouraged or started by the wildlife federations. Three of those in British Columbia are the influential Steelhead Society of British Columbia, the Sport Fishing Advisory Board (to the federal minister of fisheries) and the British Columbia Federation of Fly Fishers. The oldest of those is the Sport Fishing Advisory Board (first called "Committee"), a sixteen-person group of advisors from all over the province that meets two or three times a year as a sounding board for the Pacific regional management of recreational fishing. It examines allocation of salmon stocks between commercial and food fisheries on

149

one hand (which consumes ninety-six percent of the stock) and recreational-tourist fishermen on the other, who consume only four or five percent of the annual salmon harvest. When organizing the SFAB in 1964, Department of Fisheries Director W. Rod Hourston asked the Federation to suggest delegates to the Board, though only two were designated representatives of the Federation. Since then, the SFAB has expanded to twenty-two members and early this year was considering expansion to twenty-eight. Of the original two, the Wildlife Federation representation later was increased to eight. The other delegates are "independent" or from the sport fishing industry, but the majority of the SFAB always are "primary" users.

The Steelhead Society of B.C. was created in 1970 after a steelhead committee of the B.C. Wildlife Federation decided at its 1969 convention that it needed more specifically identifiable representation to speak for river anglers everywhere. The Society organized at a Port Coquitlam meeting in 1970 and now has a membership around eight hundred, has a central board of twenty-eight directors that meets monthly in Vancouver, plus the directors of five chapters on Vancouver Island and in the Skeena Valley.

The B.C. Federation of Fly Fishers, at last report, had sixteen clubs affiliated with it and two more thinking about it. The BCFFF was formed in the mid-seventies but wasn't registered under the Society Act until 1979. At last count, seven of their sixteen clubs were directly affiliated with the B.C. Wildlife Federation.

All these organized sportsmen, active though they are, with their combined membership around the forty-thousand mark, represent only about five percent of the angling and shooting licence-holders. That, however, seems just as great a show of interest as the average citizen exerts toward political organizations. Some people feel that the government attaches too much importance to the recommendations of organized outdoorsmen. Yet almost all our contenders for provincial or federal government positions are nominated by political associations that have a representation of only one or two percent of the voters.

Natural History Societies of B.C.

Vernon C. (Bert) Brink

In March, 1890, notices were sent to a number of British Columbia residents asking if they would be interested in forming a natural history society. Subsequently, in April, 1890, forty gentlemen formed "The Natural History Society of B.C." The creation of the new Society marked the need for a more organized approach to the study of the natural features of the province and a need for "an independent auxiliary to the Provincial Museum, Department of Agriculture, Department of Mines, and the Library of the Legislative Assembly." Victoria, in that era, was the cultural centre of British Columbia and it was not surprising that most of the members resided there. Vancouver, following a fire, was largely a town of shacks and tents. Most of the members of the Society were from the clergy, the armed services, medicine, the law or engineering. They mirrored the culture of Victorian Britain. By 1900, there were corresponding members from mainland British Columbia and other parts of the world, ladies were being admitted as ordinary members and provisions were made for seniors from public and private schools.

Wildlife, if defined broadly as the native fauna of land and sea, was the subject of many papers presented by members and guests in 1890. Some of the titles were: "Bears," "the Crabs of B.C.," "the Deer of B.C.," "Birds and What They Are," and "the Salmonidae of B.C." Other papers related to provincial geology, anthropology and engineering.

By 1900, in the rapidly growing communities of the lower Fraser Valley, the Okanagan Valley, and the Comox-Courtenay area, people in many walks of life were beginning to ask serious questions about the natural environment into which they, as new immigrants, had come. By 1907, the "Vancouver Naturalist Club" had formed, but along somewhat more egalitarian lines than its counterpart in Victoria. Groups of naturalists were also meeting in Vernon and Comox.

It is not surprising that the first naturalist's club in Vancouver was the "B.C. Mountaineering Club" and that naturalists formed a section within that club in 1910. That occurred quite amicably and simply reflected the fact that to explore a largely unknown and mountainous land was both interesting and exciting. Moreover, reaching many of the areas of high natural interest called for mountaineering skills. As World War I drew to a close, however, the B.C.M.C. natural history section joined with the Arbor Day Association and with some other small groups to form, again amicably, "the Vancouver Natural History Society"; the date was May, 1918.

The amity of the early years ended in the late 1920's when the Burrard Field Naturalists cloned off from the Vancouver Natural History Society and became associated with the Art, Historical and Scientific Association, and the Vancouver Museum. Some of the detailed studies undertaken by the Burrard naturalists focused on invertebrate zoology and anthropology. The group dissolved in the early 1940's. Both the Vancouver Natural History Society and the Burrard Field Naturalists, among their many endeavours, were supportive of the museums of the province, the Vancouver Zoo, and the life and earth sciences at the youthful University of British Columbia.

Communication between the natural history societies of British Columbia was for many years casual. After World War II, a relationship between the natural history societies of Victoria, Vancouver and Vernon (the three V's) was somewhat formalized as "the Nature Council of B.C."; the object was to promote interest in natural history in other centres of British Columbia. Indeed, other clubs joined and new clubs were started. In 1969, with a lot of drive from a retired logger, Elton Anderson, nearly all clubs united as "the Federation of B.C. Naturalists"; a constitution and motto expressing interest in both the educational and conservational: "To know nature and to keep it worth knowing," were adopted. There are today 35 clubs in the Federation and membership now stands at around 5,000 without the inclusion of the affiliates.

The remarkable developments in science and technology, and the pressures created by rapidly growing human populations after World War II were accompanied by great impacts on the natural world and changes in the attitudes of people towards wildlife. The changes and developments are not easy to document for many are only beginning to be "history." Certainly, in ways not earlier perceived, "environmental pollution," "habitat loss," and "plant and animal extinctions" became concerns of naturalists and of much of the public. Amateur naturalists were over-awed by the numbers of professionals and specialties in the natural sciences, and only now begin to realize their role as partners with scientists in the science of ecology. Natural history, too, became big business with the rise of tourism and nature tours for "every man." The varied supportive role once given to educational institutions by the natural history societies almost vanished but may be reappearing as a need for docents, wardens and other volunteers is again being met from the organized natural history societies. Recent decades, too, saw in British Columbia, and elsewhere, a proliferation of non-profit societies, many with secondary or unspecified interests in wildlife; distinctions between "naturalist," "environmentalist" and "outdoor recreationist" became blurred.

Without doubt the most powerful non-profit federated organization developing in British Columbia in the post-war years was the B.C. Wildlife Federation; its interest in wildlife is clear-cut. It developed from the rod and gun clubs, and is regarded by most naturalists, not without respect for its conservation activities, as primarily "extractive" or, as some term it, "consumptive," and as having a primary interest in game species.

By 1970, the mountaineering clubs of British Columbia had become the Federation of B.C. Mountain Clubs; their interest in wilderness protection indirectly involved them in wildlife habitat protection. It was this Federation which, with support from other groups, such as the naturalists' societies, fostered the creation of the non-profit "Outdoor Recreation Council of B.C." which now has over 40 contributing organizations. Several of these have an interest in wildlife welfare.

Many "single issue" groups, often with strong interest in wildlife and natural history have come into being in British Columbia since 1945. The Okanagan-Similkameen Parks Society is an arbitrarily chosen example. Its membership, drawn from the business community, rod and gun clubs, and naturalists' clubs, focused first on the reservation of land around Vaseaux Lake in the South Okanagan Regional District for waterfowl and native sheep; it materially assisted the Canadian Wildlife Service, the B.C. Wildlife Branch, and the Nature Trust in securing properties. The Society also fostered primary outdoor recreation by supporting the creation of Cathedral Lakes Provincial Park and other parks, and conservation of parts of the historic fur-brigade trails in southwestern British Columbia.

Distinctions between "support of" and "involvement with" wildlife and issues related to it are often blurred. Support from some groups is sometimes passive — writing letters and briefs to authorities. In some cases, clubs provide volunteers as docents or unpaid wardens. Naturalists have a long history of serving in this latter manner — providing instructors for nature and outdoor programs to scouts and guides, and other organizations, docents for the Vancouver Public Aquarium, museums or more recently wardens for the British Columbia ecological reserves and wildlife refuges. Often the initial assistance comes from the naturalist clubs and later the facilities develop their own volunteer groups. A good example would be "the B.C. Waterfowl Society" conceived by some naturalist "birders" and waterfowl hunters. Naturalists, mountaineers, and rod and gun club members, on a voluntary basis, at least since the early 1920's, have planted shrubs for birds, built and cleared nature trails and wildlife viewing platforms, erected fences, cleared fish spawning beds or otherwise engaged in wildlife habitat enhancements. Much of this kind of endeavour is now partially organized under para-governmental agencies or boards or federal-provincial employment opportunities funds.

Increasingly, naturalists and their clubs produce books, bulletins, posters, films and slide shows relating to wildlife and its habitat. Internal publications of the societies, some of which have passed the half-century mark in production, are becoming referred journals. The Vancouver Natural History Society's *Discovery*, the *B.C. Naturalist* of the Federation of B.C. Naturalists contain much information on British Columbia wildlife. Publications such as *Threatened and Endangered Species and Habitats of British Columbia and the Yukon*, produced jointly by the Federation of B.C. Naturalists and the British Columbia Ministry of Environment and Parks or *Nature West Coast* by the Vancouver Natural History Society have a wide demand.

Some forms of support by public groups are not easily defined. For example, most naturalists' societies and the thoughtful public are well aware of the scarcity of and intense competition by industry, housing, and agriculture for the low elevation lands of British Columbia. Well appreciated by naturalists, and rod and gun club members, but not yet well appreciated by the general public, or many outdoor recreationists, is the fact that most of the lowland is privately owned and that much of it is critical as winter habitat for the survival of much of our unique indigenous fauna and for migrating waterfowl. Much of the habitat in the private domain is rapidly and irretrievably being lost. Naturalists and Wildlife Federation members, since the early 1970's particularly, and increasingly in the last few years, almost alone among outdoor groups, strongly support the few agencies, acquiring by purchase or agreement, private lands; such as the Nature Trust, the Habitat Conservation Board of Canada, the Nature Conservancy of Canada and some government departments with limited opportunities to purchase land. The major efforts to designate Crown land, for example, major parks, for wildlife have tended to overlook the need for lowland and ecological balance.

There are several national and international societies in British Columbia relating to wildlife. Those seen as complementary to the provincial naturalists' clubs are the Canadian Nature Federation (since 1971), the Northwest Bird and Mammal Society (for over 50 years), the Audubon Society of America, the Western Society of Naturalists and some (since the turn of the century) humane and animal care societies. The Sierra Club of Western Canada, formed in 1969, affiliated with the Sierra Club originating in California, is acknowledged as having a wildlife conservation interest among its many environmental interests. Greenpeace, broadly activist and involved in peace movements, has objectives which subtend those of provincial naturalist clubs and is generally regarded coolly by them. Relations of the naturalists of British Columbia with the Ecological Society of America go back at least to 1917 when British Columbia naturalists co-operated with that Society's Committee on the Preservation of Natural Conditions for Ecological Study. The efforts of the committee in the 1920's resulted in the publication of at least one significant book on North American wildlife and habitats. Rapport with scientific and professional organizations faded but now, as in Great Britain, it appears in British Columbia to be in a process of re-establishment.

The last 10 or 20 years have seen the creation of a plethora of natural history, environmental and outdoor recreation, non-governmental, para-governmental and governmental groups with at least some interest in wildlife. One result is the formation of coalitions, councils and symposia with special objectives in which natural history societies play some part. One example of a coalition was R.O.S.S. (Run Out Skagit Spoilers). Fifteen years of pressure to prevent further flooding of the Canadian Skagit Valley did produce a result. Another example (of many to choose from) would be the Fraser River Coalition. It was probably initiated by actions of the now defunct Environmental Council of B.C. and the Lower Mainland Planning Board in the 1960's which pointed out the multitude of federal, provincial and regional jurisdictions (over 60) involved in the management of the Fraser River estuary and the need for better co-ordination. Among the many groups creating an awareness of the need and concern for the fishery and the waterfowl were the naturalist societies and regional colleges. The creation of reservations for wildlife and considerable improvement in jurisdictional co-ordination attended the efforts of public and government agencies. Needless to say, the need for the Fraser River Coalition continues to exist and it continues to function.

It may be useful to record some of the changes in the attitudes of organized naturalists since the first club was formed in Victoria in 1890. Many of the early naturalists of British Columbia were excellent hunters, fishermen and taxidermists, as well as being students of animals, other living things and physical features. R. J. Pop, a well-known furrier and taxidermist, was welcomed in the program of the Vancouver Natural History Society in the 1920's for his talks on British Columbia's big game animals and his trophies came to adorn the lecture hall at U.B.C. where the Society met. It is doubtful if an R. J. Pop lecture would be welcome today. In 1914, some naturalists even joined a crow shoot (crows were widely regarded as vermin) in, of all places, Stanley Park. Today, naturalists' organizations are represented on the problem animal control committee and help to draw the hard line between conserving wildlife and controlling it in the more settled areas of the province. To date, there is little overt opposition from organized naturalists to hunting and fishing, but with an awareness of the limitations of the resource, there is little confidence in the ability of Big Government to manage and to sustain the wildlife resource.

There is a tendency in public interest groups to say "we did it" when land is designated for wildlife conservation and management. In reality, governments and, in our community, elected people "do it." Naturalists, like others, have learned that the process of designation is meandering, incomplete, frustrating and often demands years of patience. At one time, most natural history societies believed that if only a park or conservancy of some kind could be created that "government" would, in its wisdom, manage the land for the benefit of wildlife and outdoor recreation. Successive changes in the boundaries of Garibaldi Park by government to remove trees for harvest and the development of a logging enterprise in the park by the Garibaldi Park Board in 1939-41 helped end their naïveté. The societies had something to do with the demise of park boards and the establishment of the provincial park system through presentation of briefs and drawing in support from groups such as the Women's Institutes and Local Council of Women. Slowly, too, it was realized that parks, once thought to be the ultimate designation for the conservation of wildlife, wilderness and passive recreation were often incomplete ecosystems. They had often failed to accommodate wildlife winter range by the arbitrary drawing of boundaries or by accommodating extractive activities such as agriculture, mining or forestry. The meanderings of multiple-use philosophy in government failed to rekindle a confidence once held by naturalists and petitions for other kinds of conservatory designations such as wildlife management areas were put forward by natural history societies, and the rod and gun clubs. After many years of discussion, in 1987, six wildlife management areas were declared under an amended Wildlife Act. In 1987, a wilderness area under an amended Forest Act was created.

Some things do not seem to change much. Prior to World War I, a lecture with "electric light lantern illustrations" given by a Scottish gamekeeper was the subject of discussion in a naturalists' meeting. The life history of the stag was reviewed; carrying capacity was given as 300 to 600 acres of forest and moor; each stag killed was recorded as having a value of 30 to 50 pounds sterling; the relative merits of ranging deer and domestic sheep were discussed. In the face of an agricultural community, it took great courage for the chairman of the Highland Railroad Co. in Scotland to state, "gentlemen, your dividend is derived from deer and grouse."

Birding is today the fashion among organized naturalists but that may be changing again with rising interest in mammals, insects, plants and physical features of British Columbia. Entomology was once a popular pursuit and a lot of fun. Something of the lively interest comes down to us from a natural history outing in 1916 led by a Mr. Sherman into the White Rock area — listed as a "sugaring expedition." A solution was concocted of a pint of sugar, a quart of beer, a dash of whiskey and with this peculiar mixture the party started on a hunt for insects. The procedure was to walk through the woods and paint the trunks of trees with this potion, putting the solution on the lee side of the trees. Thus, a slight breeze carried the scent of the booze to the insects and attracted them to the trees. Upon tasting the stuff, the poor innocent moths and beetles became pickled and fell to the ground to be collected later by their hunters. The potion was reported by some field trippers to taste "not bad." It must have been fun.

Then there was the case of the missing false teeth. In the 1950's, the Vancouver Natural History Society was still using society-owned canvas tents with several persons assigned to a tent. One camper at the Crown Lakes camp had carefully placed his set of false teeth by his blankets on retiring, but in the morning they were gone. Grumpily all day long he accused his fellow tenters of pulling a practical joke. At evening camp fire, he was presented with a set — a set made of horse teeth taken from a skull found on the range and set in mud. He took the presentation in as good humour as a toothless person could. Next morning a few botanists near camp found a pile of sticks and on top, along with a miscellany of camp items such as forks, combs, etc., was the camper's false teeth and also some nuts on which our camper had munched before retiring and which had obviously made the teeth very attractive. A practical lesson in the history of pack rats (Neotoma)!

Will the day return when wildlife officers and scientists voluntarily again join our natural history society camps?

Many will remember vividly, by way of example, a visit Ron Mackay of the Canadian Wildlife Service, paid to one of our lakeside camps a number of years ago. He canoed in at dusk with his beautiful dog and played the pipes as he stepped on the beach. Then came the handshakes and warm greetings, and the quiet as the last light faded — a quietness broken only by the muted sounds of waterfowl in the nearby reeds.

It may not be as easy for natural history societies to keep learning about wildlife and to make it the keen pleasure it was in earlier years — not in the face of the losses the natural environment is suffering but surely the motto "to know and to enjoy nature, and to keep it worth knowing" must be kept shining.

"Alas, that life must forever feed its growth on death, and human progress advance only over the ruins of the perfect!"

W. H. H. Murray, 1888
Daylight Land

When all is said and done it boils down to the land. There must be a place where wildlife can live. Without that place, or those places, there will be no wildlife. That is the simple fact of the matter.

There is no need at this stage in our story to be fancy about the solution. Habitat must be preserved, often at the expense of other useful purposes, if animals are to exist in satisfactory numbers. The man who owns the land controls wildlife. In British Columbia, with the Crown owning more than 90 percent of the land base, we the people own the land. How will we treat it so future generations can be assured that it will yield for them as generously as it has for us?

We have seen how people concerned with wildlife have come and gone in the past 100 years; naturalists, guides, hunters, law makers, law breakers, scientists, trappers. They are not the ones who have used and abused the land. It is the rest of us who, in our relentless search for a "better" standard of living, have ditched and ploughed and flooded and dug and cut down and sprayed and paved and generally despoiled habitat. But still the animals have survived, not always where we want them, or in the diversity we would like, but survived nonetheless, and in some cases prospered.

It would be comforting to think we could go on like this forever. Only the most short sighted can believe that. Each day brings us closer to the point where the land will not produce the wildlife it is capable of yielding. Each day some pieces of "our" land cease to be habitat for "our" wildlife. How did we make that choice?

CHAPTER 10

Wildlife Habitat — The Impacts of Settlement

Dennis A. Demarchi and Raymond A. Demarchi

British Columbia has a wide diversity of ecoregions as a result of its large size (948,600 square kilometres), its position (bounded on the west by the Pacific Ocean and on the east by the Interior Plains and Rocky Mountains), its varied topography and complex climatic patterns. Most typically, the province is dominated by sub-alpine, sub-boreal, boreal and maritime climates in a mountainous setting most of which is higher than 1000 metres above sea level.

Most of the 600 terrestrial wildlife and marine mammal species in the province avoid areas of deep snow. For example: the amphibians and reptiles hibernate; most bird species migrate to southern coast, desert or tropical areas; some mammals (like bears and ground-squirrels) hibernate; most ungulates and attendant predators seek areas of low snowfall with high forage productivity. In the southern part of the province, the low snow areas are in the valley bottoms or on low-elevation, south-facing slopes. In the north and in most mountain ranges, the low snow areas are wind-swept ridges which are often near the tops of the mountains. Another favoured wintering area, especially of moose, are floodplains, where the abundance of palatable forage compensates for the deeper snow conditions. Only a few animals, such as the southern caribou, the ptarmigan and wolverine seek areas of deeper snow for wintering.

For simplicity's sake, the province can be separated into five kinds of land, each with a different climate, soils, habitat and land uses: 1) *The lowlands*, which are composed of the large basins, the Rocky Mountain Trench and the Fraser Delta. They have the warmest and driest climates and the most productive soils in the province. These areas also have the most productive big game winter ranges. Unfortunately, these areas are the most sought-after for human habitation and industrial, agricultural and forestry enterprises; and for construction of transportation and utility corridors. 2) *The plateaus and valley bottoms within the mountains*. These areas are generally used as summer ranges by big game, but there is some winter-range potential along the floodplains, on the southern slopes and in the old-growth forests. The primary land use is logging. Nearly all hydro-electric reservoirs occur in this setting. Agriculture is most often marginal. Corridor development is usually for logging or mineral extraction. 3) *The southern roadless mountainous areas.* These areas are the rugged, upper mountain areas and high-elevation basins. They contain some of the most rugged and inhospitable land in the province: the Coast, the Selkirk and the Purcell mountains. There is very little human land use, except for the occasional mine. The most prevalant big game species are mountain goat, grizzly bear and black-tailed deer or mule deer. 4) *The northeast or Alberta Plateau* of the northern boreal plain. The extensive lacustrine soils coupled with the long, sub-arctic summer days are suitable for cereal grain production. This area also has productive oil and natural gas reserves. There are high-capability moose, mule deer, white-tailed deer and elk winter ranges in the Peace River Lowlands, while the uplands are used as both summer range and extensive winter range for moose and caribou. 5) *The northern wilderness.* These areas are boreal or sub-arctic mountains and plateaus. Few people live there and the few established communities are small and scattered. The main land-use practices are guide-outfitting and mining. These areas represent the largest mountain wilderness in the province and are the domain of Stone's sheep, woodland caribou, mountain goat, wolf, grizzly bear and moose.

Wildlife are vulnerable to habitat destruction by virtue of the way they use the land: they are not randomly distributed. Instead, each herd, group or individual searches out microsites for feeding, cover or homesites which, in the case of most big game species, may be far apart. Several bands of animals may flock or herd together to give an appearance of unity, yet with each component of the group searching for specific sites within the larger habitat. Often, important habitat is used for only one or two seasons and is vacant for the rest of the year. In contrast with this gentle use, man's bulldozers are indiscriminate, gouging deep furrows and straight lines. As a consequence, critical habitats can quickly become dissected, isolated or buried.

Habitat destruction is usually the result of a series of actions that are based on pre-emptive decisions, which in some cases, were initiated by the native Indians and fur traders, or even the early governors of the province. Aboriginal people entered what is now British Columbia during the period of the waning of the last great cordilleran ice-sheet, about 12,000 years ago. Their villages were established mainly along the coast and in the interior valleys, with greater populations associated with salmon bearing streams.

The first European explorers reached the shores of the province in the late 1700's and the first three overland explorers (Alexander Mackenzie, Simon Fraser and David Thompson) established trade-routes in the province during the period 1793-1808. Both oceanic and overland trade routes were quickly established, with settlements springing up at strategic points at the start of, or along, these routes. The explorers came for furs, mainly beaver and sea otter pelts, which they harvested with the assistance of the native Indians with reckless abandon. Attempts at other resource use were slow until the mid-1800's, when placer gold was discovered in several places in the province. Then miners, mainly from the worked-over gold fields in California, began to work these new finds. When the difficult realities of gold mining became apparent, many of the miners turned to agriculture, forestry or fishing, rather than return to their native lands.

With the development of commercial steam locomotives, British Columbia was wooed into the confederation of Canada with the promise of a cross-country railroad link. The price was the biggest land give-away in our history. The province could not afford to pay for the building of the railroad with cash. Instead it gave away land, a belt 32.2 kilometres wide on either side of the Canadian Pacific Railroad mainline, plus 1,416,000 hectares in the Peace River block. When some of that land proved unsatisfactory, other land on Vancouver Island and in the Kootenays was offered in trade. Although not all of the original land was subsequently alienated, and by 1930 about 60 percent was returned to the province, the intent of the land give-away was clear — massive colonization.

Historically, the land-use philosophy in British Columbia was based on satisfying the individual Euro/Asian immigrant's needs within the overall objective to "... develop and settle the land." The province pursued this objective by allowing individuals and corporations almost free access to resources. Progress was measured by the number of acres alienated and "improved" each year. As both the public and politicians alike believed that benefits would automatically accrue from any resource use, legislation and policies were devised to facilitate rather than regulate resource development and exploitation.

Fortunately, the constitutional arrangements of British Columbia's entry into confederation endowed the province with almost all of the land owned by the Crown. The concept of public ownership of land and private access to timber resources originated in land ordinances issued before 1864 by James Douglas, Governor of the Crown Colony of Vancouver Island. This policy continued when Vancouver Island and the mainland were united as a colony in 1866 and later, 1871, when the colony joined Confederation. These concepts remain the cornerstone of much of the current B.C. Ministry of Forests and Lands' forest management policy. British Columbians today, as well as future generations, owe much to the foresight of this one individual,

161

who sought to prevent speculators from gaining control and exploiting the province's forest wealth.

Development and settlement objectives were paramount, however. For much of the province's early history there was no attempt at multiple resource use. Land development and resource extraction proceeded on a first-order, single-objective basis. Forests were burned to better locate mineral outcrops. Land was cleared of trees in order to farm it (even in places that had no access to markets). Land was given over to development companies for single-purpose use and those companies were given virtually the entire province from which they could make their selections which, in the case of the railroad companies, were often not close to the location of their rail lines. Land was mined, farmed, flooded, logged and built-upon, with little consideration given the effects on fisheries, forestry or wildlife.

In the late 1960's, the Environment and Land Use Committee of cabinet was struck as a forum to resolve resource conflicts at the highest political level. Since 1971, the committee has been guided by the Environment and Land Use Act. The basic concept "... is to ensure that all aspects of preservation and maintenance of the natural environment are fully considered in the administration of land use and resource development, commensurate with a maximum beneficial land use..." In other words, multiple resource use. Most recently the prevailing attitude has seen a shift in this concept to one of integrated resource use, where certain specific uses may become paramount in some cases. This is the first step towards recognizing that wildlife values may take precedence over other resources, or may be considered to be the primary use, among other resource uses compatible with wildlife habitat management.

In order to preserve our wildlife heritage we must preserve the habitat on which the wildlife depends. There are no easy answers. Society demands "progress," governments want tax revenue, business wants the freedom to ply its trades and, yet, there is still a desire, by the public, to have wildlife and wilderness. So we must establish methods of interjecting habitat protection and maintenance into the institutions that demand land for their uses. This is no easy task. Our development practices have developed over generations but our preservation instincts are relatively new. Wildlife must be recognized by all parties — its value as well as its use. We have a heritage and resource worth perpetuating, but we must make major inroads into the old philosophy of single-use resource extraction. In order to do this, we must examine the causes of habitat loss.

We have outlined six classes of major intrusions onto the wildlife habitat base. They can be considered as separate issues, yet they are connected in that they serve the growing demands of an ever increasing population. We also look at how habitat is being preserved through planning processes; the role of parks and other wildland reserves, always mindful of the activities of both government and the private sector, in protecting wildlife habitat in British Columbia.

Agriculture

There are two basic types of agricultural practice in the province: the intensive cultivation of crops which are often associated with intensive husbandry of livestock (farming), and the extensive free-ranging of livestock (ranching).

Intensive agriculture is a form of land use which pre-empts both forestry and most native species of wildlife. Conflicts between agriculture and other renewable resource interests occur throughout the world, wherever agro-cultivation or intensive livestock grazing is practiced. Compared with forest, fisheries, mineral, petroleum, wildlife, water and recreational resources, British Columbia's agricultural capabilities are severely limited. Because of topography, climate and pattern of human settlement, however, the conflicts between agriculture and wildlife are particularly severe in this province.

Major permanent settlement of the province followed the limited patches and ribbons of arable soil on southern Vancouver Island, the Lower Mainland (i.e.; Fraser River Delta), the Southern Interior (i.e., Okanagan, Thompson, Columbia and Kootenay River benchlands), the Central Interior (i.e., Fraser, Nechako and Bulkley River basins), and the Boreal Plain (i.e., Peace River basin).

Following a period of scattered, initial settlement based on the fur trade, gold mining, coastal logging and commercial fishing, and the granting of the Railroad Belt Lands for alienation, a major boom in land alienation and settlement occurred during the late 1890's and early 1900's. By 1913, more than one million hectares of land were alienated to agriculture.

The second and third waves of land settlement occurred in the 1920's and the 1940's when land was made readily available to veterans of the First and Second World Wars. With the most productive land already alienated, these homestead endeavours occurred in the climatically more marginal areas in the central and northeastern parts of the province and on peripheral upland areas throughout the Southern Interior. A significant percentage of these attempts ended in failure, while those who occupied the best sites managed modest returns.

Despite the harsh lessons of the two post-World-Wars settlement programs, another intensive program to "... develop British Columbia's agriculture" was initiated between the early 1960's and early 1970's. Land alienations increased markedly, particularly in central and northeastern British Columbia. Between 1961 and 1970, inclusive, a further 1.1 million hectares of Crown land, largely productive timber and wildlife resource lands, were leased (divided almost equally into arable land and grazing leases).

Expansion and development of agriculture have proceeded with the aid and support of massive public subsidies, including federal and provincial tax incentives, many of which continue to date. These lands were alienated by the B.C. Lands Service at bargain basement prices, and the B.C. Department of Agriculture encouraged and promoted development, irrespective of capability, via subsidized land clearing and production loans. Thus, as well as destroying valuable timber and wildlife assets, marginal farming enterprises of low agricultural yield continued at enormous public expense, displaying a lack of economic as well as ecological logic.

The more than two million hectares of land alienated to single-use agriculture to date include some of the province's most productive timber growing sites as well as being situated on critical valley-bottom winter habitats for elk, white-tailed deer, mule deer and moose, and seasonally important habitats for a large variety of bird and mammal species.

Early farming practices enhanced some species of native wildlife by creating relatively small, forage-producing openings, surrounded by forests. Exotic bird species such as Chinese ring-necked pheasant and Hungarian partridge flourished until the advent of modern "clean" farming practices. The exigencies of agricultural expansion required the eradication of predators, such as wolves and grizzlies, and the reduction and control of cougars, coyotes, black bears and beaver. In addition, there has been drainage of wetlands, including floodplains, estuaries and extensive marshes and the channelization of streams. Sumas Lake (now Sumas Prairie), Creston Flats and the Fraser River Delta are examples.

Livestock grazing, namely horses herded by native Indians, predated British Columbia Euro/Asian settlement by a century or more. Early attempts at developing a domestic sheep industry resulted in extensive damage to fragile, low elevation as well as alpine grasslands in the southern interior, including the Yalakom and Ashnola valleys, accompanied by the introduction of diseases, such as sore-mouth and pneumonia, to Rocky Mountain bighorn sheep herds in the East Kootenay. Destruction of predators, such as grizzly bears, wolves and coyotes was a matter of course. Fortunately for wildlife interests, the dropping of import quotas for foreign mutton and wool resulted in the collapse of the sheep industry, thus removing one of the greatest threats to wildlife in the province.

Beef cattle ranching has been practiced in southern British Columbia for well over 100 years. Ranchers situated on private, arable, valley bottom lands have traditionally been given access to forage on

Crown land in the form of highly subsidized, annually renewable, grazing permits, or the longer term, grazing leases. The expansion of cattle ranching in southern British Columbia, including the Cariboo-Chilcotin, Thompson-Nicola, Okanagan-Similkameen and East Kootenay, resulted in overgrazing and, in some cases, ecosystem degradation of native grassland and seral shrubland communities. Wildlife species dependent on climax-grassland such as sharp-tailed grouse, burrowing owls and long-billed curlews were locally extirpated, while cattle competition with wild ungulates was severe.

More recently, improved grazing systems have been employed to lessen the impacts of livestock grazing and to begin the long process of range restoration. The Ministry of Forests and Lands currently estimates that Crown range annually supports 200,000 cow/calf pairs and yearlings during the summer grazing period. (Although international trade exists, Canada is neither a net importer or net exporter of beef. British Columbia produces four percent of Canada's beef, but consumes 10 percent. Approximately three quarters of British Columbia's beef production comes from cultivated lands and one quarter from improved pasture and rangelands. Thus, less than one percent of Canada's beef production comes from British Columbia's rangelands.)

In regions where native forage is limited by poor grass-growing conditions, such as the Omineca and Peace River regions, the cattle industry has been provided forage in the form of community pastures. Vegetative shelter and escape cover can be removed without consideration given to wildlife. Browse species, important to wild ungulates but unpalatable to cattle, are eliminated by the use of herbicides or burning, and the available forage is grazed to capacity by cattle. In addition, the removal of predatory wildlife is pursued to the extent that total extermination is requested in most instances involving wolves or grizzlies. Highly subsidized and intensively managed by clearing, brushing, seeding, prescribed burning and herbiciding, these pastures conflict with the province's now stated, multiple land use policy. Thus, community pastures represent single (agricultural) use of an area at the expense of renewable wildlife and forest resource values.

The discussion of the impacts of agriculture on wildlife habitat would not be complete without a brief mention of agricultural chemicals and biocides. The extensive use of pesticides, particularly the chlorinated hydro-carbons such as DDT and Chlordane, severely affected predatory bird species as well as other species of wildlife and, in some instances, threatened man, as foretold by Rachel Carson in her book, *Silent Spring*. The species most affected — the peregrine falcon — was near extinction, while several other species of raptor suffered severe declines before the use of DDT was halted in the province as well as the rest of Canada and the U.S.A. in 1972.

British Columbia supports slightly more than one fifth of the nation's forest land, yet generates two-fifths of the harvest of merchantable timber. Each year some of the 150,000 hectares of the provincial forest land base are logged under the Ministry of Forests and Lands' sustained yield, forest management policy, and an additional 50-70,000 hectares are burned by accidental, planned or natural causes.

In British Columbia, less than five percent of the productive forest land is privately owned. By far the largest share of the Crown land is within Provincial Forests, under the Forest Act (81.1 million hectares, or 86 percent of the province's total area). The Ministry of Forests and Lands estimates that only about 21.3 million hectares (24 percent) are actually available and suitable for commercial forest production. (Estimates of the amount of productive forest land in B.C. vary, depending upon the assumptions chosen in determining economic accessibility, as influenced by terrain, productivity, distance to market, etc.)

Logging and burning are responsible for significant changes in wildlife distribution and abundance as a result of changes in the structural component of the habitat (i.e., shelter) and plant communities (i.e., food). The effects range from calamitous to highly beneficial, depending upon the species and habitat involved. The complex mosaic of species and habitat niches precludes generalizations. Forest harvesting which displaces one or more species often leads to major improvements in habitat conditions for other species. Certain species such as woodland caribou, pine marten and pileated woodpeckers are dependent upon old growth or mature (often climax) forests, while other species such as moose, snowshoe hares and blue grouse do best in seral shrublands. Logging or burning, which remove the forest canopy, exposes the soil surface to sunlight and releases nutrients, which increases growth of herbaceous plants. Thus, while the habitat of old-growth, forest-dependent species may be destroyed by logging or fire, other species that are dependent upon early seral communities often benefit. Generalizations, even among climax or seral species, are often misleading, as some species may require either old-growth or seral communities, depending upon such factors as human disturbance, snow-depth and duration, winter and summer temperatures and season of use.

The arguments that logging benefits wildlife or even that "good logging is good for wildlife" are dangerously misleading. The great diversity and complexity of habitats and wildlife requirements in British Columbia, coupled with the complexities of individual species or population requirements, make it essential that wildlife requirements be incorporated into operational-level forest management.

Adherence to a policy of optimum sustained yield is gradually replacing the philosophy of maximum sustained yield. The Ministry of Forests Act and the Forest Act of 1978 make the Ministry of Forests and Lands legally responsible and accountable for the maintenance of wildlife habitat, as well as wood fibre production, recreation and forage for livestock.

Maintenance of the current annual allowable production of wood fibre is dependent upon the early detection and suppression of wildfire and the shortening of the time interval between timber harvesting and regeneration of new forests.

In British Columbia, as in the rest of North America, a major objective of forest management has been the control and elimination of wildfire. Long recognized by wildlife ecologists as an essential element in the maintenance of natural ecosystems, fire has only recently been recognized by some foresters as a useful tool in the management of the province's fire-dependent forests. The exclusion of natural fires in fire-dependent ecosystems often results in vegetation communities which are of low value to wildlife. In addition, the accumulation of fuels which would have undergone normal, periodic burning can result in severe holocausts that can impair long-term productivity by destroying the soil base. Fortunately, logging and prescribed burning can replace natural wildfires on most sites.

The province's productive forest land base is shrinking as a result of industrial and urban demands, such as hydro-electric reservoirs, transmission lines, highways, subdivisions and agricultural expansion. Losses through fire, insects and disease, although accounted for are not predictable, and there is increased pressure on the government to protect the last remaining primitive areas. Thus, the current thrust is to intensify forest management on smaller land bases.

Shortening the time-lag between timber harvesting and forest regeneration is the aim and responsibility of silviculturalists. As forest management becomes more intensive, rotation intervals may become shorter. High-yield forestry will eliminate some of the natural, successional stages to the short-term benefit of a few wildlife species but to the disadvantage of many. Wildlife impacts of such intensive forestry will include: 1) the reduction of the time interval and supply of herbaceous vegetation production and the associated "seral" wildlife species such as blue grouse, black-tailed deer, elk, moose, and black bear; 2) a more rapid elimination of old growth forest habitats affecting such species as woodland caribou and pine martin and, 3) the elimination of standing and potential snag trees, thus affecting some 24 species of cavity-dependent birds and mammals.

The effects of forestry on wildlife circumstance in the province are potent, although not nearly so adverse as some speculate. Integrated land-use planning, including access management, reclamation, fire management and wilderness preservation, while in the initial stages, is slowly emerging as government policy. The combined task of wildlife biologists, ecologists and foresters is to integrate wildlife requirements into forest management in order to protect and maintain the public's interest in both.

Hydro-electric Development

Impounding of streams and rivers for hydro-electric power generation is a twentieth century phenomenon. The first registered power dam in British Columbia was built in 1903 on Trout Creek in North Vancouver. Prior to that, dams were built for water storage. (The first registered dam was the water storage dam built in 1895 on Goldstream Creek in Victoria.) At first, dams for power or water storage were small and were located adjacent to the area of need. By 1951, there still were only 61 registered dams with 6,581 million cubic metres of water impounded. It was during the late 1940's and 1950's that the megadams became politically popular. The Campbell River was twice dammed, in 1949 and 1958; the Nechako River twice, in 1952 and 1953, and the Bridge River twice, in 1955 and 1960. By 1961, the number of registered dams in the province increased by 21 but the amount of storage increased almost tenfold to 66 billion cubic metres of water storage and that was only the beginning. The 1960's saw a rash of dam construction. The signing of the Columbia River Treaty between Canada and the United States of America resulted in the construction of the Duncan, High Arrow, Libby and Mica dams on the Columbia River, and the subsequent flooding of the Mac-Naughton, Keenleyside, and Koocanusa Reservoirs. It also provided the financial where-with-all to construct the W. A. C. Bennett dam creating the Williston Reservoir. By 1981, there were 103 registered dams, with 177 billion cubic metres of water stored and over 426,000 hectares of valley bottom and riparian habitat within British Columbia flooded. With technological advancement in power transmission, most of the big dams were, for the first time, able to be located considerable distances from the power users.

The impounding of a stream or river has a great impact on the movement of riverine fishes, especially anadromous fish. The dams are barriers to fish moving upstream, and fry moving downstream are often sucked through the turbines to die. The impacts on terrestrial wildlife may not be so dramatic, except when a reservoir blocks a migration route, and the animals try to cross, then drown. The direct impact on wildlife is the loss of critical habitat. The lower valley slopes, terraces and floodplains are the most productive forage-producing areas within our mountainous province. They are often the most snowfree in a valley system; yet those are the places that may

168

be flooded. For example, with the construction of the W. A. C. Bennett Dam, 178,000 hectares of prime habitat for 12,000 moose were flooded under the Williston Reservoir. The animals could not simply relocate themselves upslope. Habitat that existed above the flood line was already fully occupied by animals but, most important, much of the critical habitat for winter survival is now beneath the reservoir.

The direct influence of a dam on a river is not confined to the reservoir; the downstream flood regime is also greatly altered. For most hydro-electric projects, the purpose of the reservoir is to store water during periods of runoff, for use during low flow periods. A natural river has periods of flooding, siltation, erosion and quiesence. Under the control of a dam, a river no longer has such a cycle. In such cases, the downstream floodplains become stagnant. The most dramatic example of this was when the W. A. C. Bennett Dam first blocked the Peace River affecting the Peace/Athabasca Delta. Wetland ecosystems in Alberta were reduced in size and productivity. The consequence was reduced waterfowl and muskrat numbers. This effect also happened in the Canada goose staging area on the Nechako River, downstream from the Kenney Dam; to the Creston Flats on the Kootenay River, downstream from the Libby Dam; and invariably all other rivers in the province that have been dammed.

Mining

British Columbia's mineral, gravel, coal and petroleum resources, combined, rank second after forestry in economic importance. Although the first recorded commercial mining in the province was for coal near Nanaimo in 1835, the promise of wealth from gold played the most important role in the early development and settlement of the province. Between 1855 and 1898, no fewer than 12 major gold camps sprang up in the Interior, from the bars on the lower Fraser River in the south, through the gold-rich streams of the Cariboo, to the Wildhorse River in the East Kootenay, to Atlin in the far north. The construction of such transportation links as the Dewdney Trail (1860-65), the Cariboo Road (1861-64), the Canadian Pacific Railroad (1885) and the White Pass and Yukon Railroad (1898) coincided with the early mineral developments of the province.

Prospectors, miners, suppliers and speculators spread over the province in search of their El Dorado. With few agricultural enterprises to support them, the miners depended heavily on wild game and fish. Habitat impacts from early prospecting and mining included widespread forest fires, deliberately set to facilitate prospecting, and the logging of virgin forests for the lumber and timbers required for the construction of towns, bridges, railroad ties and mine props. In the early decades of mining the impacts were relatively minor. It was

169

not until the advent of hydraulic mining for gold on the Quesnel River in 1893 that mining began to cause serious damage to fisheries and wildlife habitat.

Development of coal deposits on Vancouver Island near Nanaimo (1869) and Fernie (1895), and major mineral deposits at Nelson, Sandon, Kimberly, Princeton, Moyie, Rossland, Riondel, Ladysmith, Greenwood and Bralorne, between 1887 and 1896, resulted in localized habitat disturbance, some of which was short-lived, as some mines were quickly depleted and others became long-lasting when mining was expanded. While most of those early mining ventures were underground operations, the impacts caused by the attendant infrastructure, including communities, extended well beyond the immediate mine workings. In addition, smelters constructed at Riondel (1894), Greenwood (1895) and Trail (1898) resulted in extensive "fume kill" of forests from toxic acid rain pollution.

The province's first open-pit coal mine was developed near Corbin in the Fernie Creek Basin during the Second World War. Shortlived, because of the conversion of ships and locomotives from coal to oil, the Corbin operation foreshadowed the massive open-pit coal mines which were to open up in the Fernie Basin, beginning with Westar's (formerly Kaiser Coal) Balmer Mine near Sparwood. The use of coal in the manufacture of steel led to new markets, resulting in the mega-coal-mining projects of southeastern and northeastern British Columbia. New towns, railroads, highways and coal preparation plants were located in the productive big game habitats of the Elk and Kootenay valleys in the southeast, and the Sukunka and Murray valleys in the northeast. As well, associated seaport facilities were built on the Fraser River estuary.

The conversion to open-pit operations greatly expanded the zones of wildlife habitat destruction around several mineral mines in the province, which for decades had operated underground, with only a few portals and waste dumps. Mining also had been confined to the higher grade deposits because of the nature of underground ore removal. With the advent of massive open-pit mining, low-grade deposits suddenly became economical. The twenty-five years between 1955 and 1979 saw a boom in open-pit mining, as such behemoths as Bethlehem Copper, Craigmont, Lornex and Valley Copper of the Highland Valley, Brenda, Endako, Afton and Numont Mines were brought into production.

The intensive localized impacts of open-pit mining render habitat protection and enhancement difficult and, in some instances, impossible. Relative to other land uses such as logging or farming, the land base involved in mining is relatively small. Open-pit mining and overburden-dumping, however, not only alter but can completely destroy the existing wildlife habitat. Other than the improvement of adjacent, or nearby, alternate habitat that may present opportunities for enhancement, the only other effective means of reducing the impacts are to design the mines' layouts and operations so as to minimize the surface area utilized and to reduce the time during which the land is unuseable by wildlife through progressive minesite reclamation.

The province's petroleum resources appear so far to be limited to the northeastern region, with some possible natural gas deposits remaining to be discovered in the southeast and offshore. Petroleum product development is usually confined to drill sites, collection networks and preparation plants, including refineries. Distribution networks, usually in the form of buried pipelines, cause disturbance of wildlife habitat by disrupting the continuity of ecological units because of increased vehicular access, and the extent to which the ground must be disturbed in order to lay the pipe.

The habitat of marine mammals remains largely intact along the 27,000 kilometres coastline of the province. Offshore drilling for oil and gas presents a high degree of pollution risk, however, in the form of blow-outs, pipeline ruptures and tanker accidents, which have to be weighed against the benefits of discovery and development of the petroleum resources.

Perhaps the most disruptive and often destructive influence of the mining and petroleum industries is in the exploration phase. Mining and petroleum legislation, which antedates the Forest Act or the Enviroment Act, requires annual expenditures or "improvements" to claims and leases, in order to maintain them in good standing. The Alberta Plateau and Liard Plain, and many of the high elevation valleys and alpine basins in the southern Rockies, as well as the coal-bearing formations of the northwestern, northeastern and southeastern regions of the province, are gridded with seismic trails or laced with exploration roads. One company alone, Kaiser Coal, bulldozed more than 250 kilometres of trails in an area of 20,000 hectares of subalpine and alpine wildlife habitat in the Fernie Basin between 1969 and 1971.

Since the mid 1970's destructive mineral, coal and petroleum inventory methods have been gradually replaced with more careful planning and the application of less destructive exploration technology. In addition, some sectors of the industry, particularly coal, have begun to reclaim the roads and trails to restore them to their former usefulness as watersheds, forests and wildlife habitat. The proper focus and action required changes in the legislation governing the maintenance of claims and leases and the inventorying of minerals, coal and petroleum resources. This was brought about simply by the inclusion of a habitat reclamation clause in all exploration and development permits. Currently, any exploration activity using me-

171

chanical equipment needs to be bonded for reclamation purposes. However, there remains a considerable backlog of exploration roads, trails and trenches which require reclamation by the province.

Transportation and Utility Corridors

Transportation and utility corridors are what we use to link our communities or to transport our resources. Native people travelled by trails and canoe-routes and the fur traders developed the trade routes and built forts at strategic locations for the movement of goods. Early roads and trail systems in the province mainly followed the river systems. When trails were built to the gold fields, they went overland, because goods were transported by pack and wagon trains. From those new roads and the old trails, our present system of corridors developed.

There are five main types of transportation and utility corridors in the province: highways, resource extraction roads, railroads, power transmission lines, and pipelines.

Highways are used to link communities. They may be freeways, linking British Columbia with other parts of Canada or the U.S.A. or they may be service roads, linking smaller communities with larger supply centres. They are often located in important habitats such as floodplains (level grades) or south- and west-facing slopes (maximum winter sunlight), or they dissect migration routes. As the speed and volume of traffic have increased, the number of animals killed by traffic also has increased to the point where, on some ranges, highway deaths are the bulk of wildlife mortality. Highways can also occupy habitat, hence remove it from use. As well, the location of some highways means that the habitat may become dissected, with some sites isolated from further use. Large freeways are a barrier to the movement of animals, by their massive road-cuts, side-casting and median dividers. In 1986 there were 45,570 kilometres of provincial roads, of which 21,100 kilometres were paved rural highways.

Resource extraction roads in British Columbia are most commonly built for either logging or mining purposes. In the case of timber access, they are usually built to maximize the exposure of forests to harvest potential, penetrating each watershed to the operable harvest limits. Trunk roads are often built to highway specifications, without asphalt capping. Once built, logging roads are kept open for silviculture and fire control. Access for mineral exploration or extraction was most often gained from roads built for logging purposes. During the past two decades, roads have been built in the northern, boreal mountain region solely to facilitate mineral exploration and mining. There is no complete inventory of all the resource extraction roads in the province.

Railroads are often located along the floodplains and lower slopes to obtain level grades. Such locations, which are critical habitats to many species of big game, mean there is constant opportunity for animal/vehicle collisions. Railroads, also, can dissect important habitat, which precludes the use of some critical sites. In 1981, there were 7,300 kilometres of mainline railroads in the province, which represents an increase of three percent on the 1960 total. In the past decade, new railroads have been laid to the coalfields in northeastern and southeasten British Columbia and the cross-country rail links are being upgraded and double-tracked. Old railroads in the Okanagan, Kettle Valley and Vancouver Island are being abandoned and their railbeds usually converted to rural or urban uses. Thus, while there does not appear to be much of an increase in railroad construction, wildlife habitat is still being altered for this purpose.

Power transmission lines can be located adjacent to roads and highways for ease of maintenance but, with the advent of the mega-dams, power transmission lines have become too large to follow existing transportation corridors and now are located on cross-country routes. There is considerable disturbance from the construction of the towers and access roads. The forest beneath the power lines is usually cleared, which results in strips of habitat kept in a treeless state by the application of herbicides, leaving limited habitat management opportunity. In 1982, there were 18,800 kilometres of power line (greater than 20,000 volts), which represents a 169 percent increase since 1960.

Pipelines for the transmission of natural gas or oil tend to avoid settlements and existing transportation corridors because of the disruptive nature of pipelines and the cost of expropriating land. Instead, they are located cross-country. Pipeline clearings are linear, and therefore the original habitat is greatly disturbed by the digging of a trench in which to bury a pipe, and by the development of access roads from which to maintain the pipe. Vegetation is also kept in a herbaceous, rather than treed state by the application of herbicides, thus severely limiting wildlife habitat management options. In 1983, there were 7,750 kilometres of oil and gas trunk and transmission lines, which is 70 percent greater than in 1960.

Urban Settlement

Settlement in British Columbia began with the aboriginal people. Their population centres were often used by the fur traders to locate forts. Most of the major communities that are established in the province have their origins with such aboriginal settlements.

Since the first Euro/Asian settlers and the subsequent reduction in the population of native Indians, the province's population has of course grown through immigration and childbirth. In 1870, there were only 36,200 people living here. By 1891 there were 98,173. By 1911 there were 390,000. The province reached one million between 1951 and 1956. The population doubled again to two million by 1976. The latest population figures show that in 1986 there were 2,889,000 people in the province. By 1990 the population is expected to be well above three million.

As population increases, communities expand. Adjacent, rural areas incorporate into the towns and cities. Much of this is agricultural land. Invariably, it was wildlife habitat. Rural activities such as farming (both productive agriculture and hobby farming) have been pushed by the new communities onto land which was habitat. In British Columbia (excluding the Alberta Plateau region), from 1971 to 1981 there were 38,500 hectares of rural land converted to urban use. By 1981, 276,000 hectares were under urban or rural settlement in the province. Associated with this occupancy was 219,000 hectares served by rural transportation. The total increase in urban/rural transportation land occupancy since 1951 is 95 per cent.

Integrated Resource Management

While the Wildlife Branch of the provincial Ministry of Environment and Parks has the responsibility of protecting and managing the province's wildlife resources, it has little control over the land base upon which wildlife depends. Much of the province's land base is either controlled by other government agencies (92 per cent) or privately owned (7.5 per cent). Even on the best habitat where the land has been assigned to the Wildlife Branch (less than one per cent) prior resource commitments, such as timber or range, impedes wildlife habitat management. Thus a major component of the Ministry of Environment and Parks' management strategy is its participation in co-operative planning processes with other government agencies and with private developers.

Resource legislation and government ministries are designed to promote individual resource management and development goals. Often such goals are contradictory or conflicting, requiring senior government intervention for resolution. Yet, no formal process exists whereby individual agency objectives may be integrated into overall operational plans. The adoption of an overall provincial land-use planning policy still eludes us. Until such a process is adopted by the government, wildlife habitat will be protected and managed only on a local, piecemeal basis.

Despite the absence of a provincial resource planning mandate, a number of operational planning processes are open to input by the provincial wildlife habitat biologists. Three of the main, current

174

examples include: 1) the interagency referral process, 2) co-ordinated resource management planning and, 3) timber supply area planning. While the first is evenly applied throughout the province, it is designed primarily to minimize and not to prevent damage to other resource interests, including wildlife. The second process, while successful in one or two regions, is not evenly pursued throughout the province and is used largely as a livestock range/wildlife planning process. More important, like other planning procedures, it lacks a mandate from senior government. The third system offers opportunities for protecting and enhancing wildlife habitat, particularly since the Ministry of Forests Act and the Forests Act require the Forest Service to integrate wildlife habitat and other resources into timber harvest plans.

Vehicular access has had profound impacts on wildlife habitats throughout the province, particularly in the southern two-thirds. Until recently, the thrust of forest and mining interests was to construct and maintain roads with little or no incentive to regulate other access or to reclaim road surfaces and rights-of-way. A co-ordinated, interagency, access management planning process was formally adopted in 1987, which establishes a format that rationalizes access construction and creates a balance between access construction and reclamation.

A wildland planning strategy was introduced as a pilot project in southeastern British Columbia in 1987. This planning initiative was an outgrowth of the Wilderness Advisory Committee's 1986 report to the Minister of Environment and Parks, and was intended to "assess the present system of wildland reserves in the East Kootenay and to recommend any changes or additions to this system, to meet wilderness tourism, recreation, wildlife and aesthetic amenities." Another example of land resource planning is the Trench Resource Integrated Plan, which is intended to designate land uses in the Rocky Mountain Trench of the East Kootenay, among forestry, livestock (range) and wildlife habitat.

Parks and Other Wildland Reserves

The province and the federal government have been setting aside lands for park purposes in British Columbia since Yoho National Park was established in 1886. There are several types of park:

National parks, established and regulated by the federal government. There are five such parks and South Moresby Islands will be the sixth.

Provincial parks, established and regulated by the provincial government. They are divided into Class A Parks—recreation only, no trapping or logging, but hunting and big game guiding are allowed and Recreation Areas and Class B Parks are managed for recreation but may have commercial resource extraction. Nature Conservancies are areas where trails are rustic, and no motorized equipment, vehicles or hunting are permitted. In addition, there are two Wilderness Parks or Conservancies.

Ecological reserves are established to protect examples of the various ecosystems of the province, as well as sites of importance to rare plants and animals. Most do not represent large ecosystems (Gladys Lake Ecological Reserve is the exception).

The Wildlife Branch has acquired some land through a variety of means such as transfers from the Lands Branch, mitigation, private donations, lease-back arrangements and outright purchases. Lands have also been similarly purchased or leased to the Canadian Wildlife Service for their management.

In recent years there has been a growing concern for establishing wilderness reserves in the remaining roadless areas of the province. This wilderness concern is compatible with other wildlife habitat concerns, but does not replace it. They are separate issues, often articulated by the same people. A good network of wilderness areas in the province will not assure proper protection of valley bottom lands, where most of the conflicting land uses occur. And, conversely, the establishment of wilderness areas should not have to wait until proper land use planning occurs in the valley bottoms and settled areas of the province. They remain two distinct issues.

Parks are usually only samples of ecosystems. They are never large enough or numerous enough to preserve all the ecoregions in a province or state. They serve the function of preserving components of ecosystems in a "natural" or unimpeded state. Unfortunately, natural wildfires are nearly always excluded, so that the forests that are represented are artificially maintained. Thus, even within forests that are represented by parks, there is not a full variety of successional forests from shrublands to old-growth, which should be there to provide the habitat of a wide variety of animal species. Parks have traditionally been established in the rugged wilderness. Sought are areas of spectacular alpine, glacier and mountain-top vistas and the adjacent sub-alpine forests of mountain hemlock on the Coast, plus Englemann spruce representing the dry montane forests, large floodplains or grasslands.

All such lands and administrative systems should be considered as complementary, even though individual agency policies and objectives may vary. This is one of the two ways in which wildlife habitat can be preserved and managed. The other way is through integrated planning. The mosaic covers a variety of ecosystems. It falls short, however, by not being co-ordinated by senior government. These

176

lands are constantly being examined by the private sector with the aim of deleting or modifying policy to allow commercial development, logging and mining.

Who Speaks for Wildlife Habitat?

We have looked at how the wildlife habitat base is being eroded and how, through integrated resource planning and land purchases, some of the habitat remains productive for wildlife. We conclude this chapter with a look at just who has been protecting this habitat: wildlife management and protection staff of the Wildlife Branch and their forerunners in the Fish and Wildlife Branch and the Fish and Game Branch have been at the forefront in protecting wildlife habitat. At the top of the list are the people and groups who, through user fees and taxation, have supported the Wildlife Branch's funding; the organized sportsmen of local clubs or the parent body, the British Columbia Wildlife Federation. In the past they have taken on the large issues such as dam construction and overgrazing. The sportsman-funded Ducks Unlimited (Canada) has played a key role in managing wetlands for waterfowl by assuring adequate water supplies for those wetlands as well as for any licenced water user. The guide/outfitters have recently become active in wilderness and land use issues. Every year, provincial hunters and fishermen pay a surtax into the Habitat Conservation Fund, which goes towards the purchase and enhancement of both fish and wildlife habitat. Similarly, there is a surcharge on the purchase of the federal migratory game bird hunting permit which goes to Wildlife Habitat Canada to purchase important wildlife habitats. Looking to the future, if wildlife habitat is to be maintained in the face of ever-increasing economic growth, the community of interest between government and non-government forces just described must grow even stronger. A strong base of public support is required to ensure the well being of the province's wildlife habitat for future generations of British Columbians.

"Whether you will or not
You are a King, Tristam, for you are one
Of the time-tested few that leaves the world,
When they are gone, not the same place it was.
Mark what you leave."

Edward Arlington Robinson
Tristam

Epilogue

Allan Murray

British Columbia is still vastly rich in wildlife. We have squandered some wildlife to be sure, but we are not bankrupt. Much habitat remains and the population of many species is strong. Indeed, some species are more abundant now than ever before. However, that should not fool us into thinking everything is all right.

The bellwether species — grizzlies, woodland caribou, and bighorn sheep are vulnerable. They are bellwether because, like the domestic sheep on whose neck is hung the bell to warn of danger, the well-being of these species is a warning of things to come. If we do not preserve habitat for these animals, if we do not enact suitable safeguards for their procreation they may well not survive. But if we can preserve them we can save all our wildlife.

One story has it that a rich ruler asked his wise men for a compilation of all the world's knowledge of economics. They returned with many volumes which proved too much for the ruler. Reduce them to key facts, he instructed, but when the economists returned they still had several volumes. The ruler was impatient and sent them back with orders to capture just the pith of all the theories of economics. They finally came back with just one line: "There's no such thing as a free lunch."

Wildlife is no free lunch. We must pay for its survival by giving up some opportunities for other uses of the land. Not all other uses must be lost, but in some cases there is little tolerance for rival use. Some species are so site specific they cannot abide crowding or other competition for the habitat. To save the wildlife we must save the habitat however valuable it may be for other uses.

One thing is certain, the land will survive. It may be robbed of fertility, its configuration may be changed, its inhabitants may be gone, but the land will remain and it will rebuild a tenant population. Indeed, man himself may be gone by this time, but the land will remain and new and maybe different species will emerge in the millennia ahead. Ultimately, we are all creatures of the land and the water. It is arrogant to think we can dig, shovel, burn, flood, drain and poison the land and water and not pay a price for it. Despoiling the land can be a costly lunch.

We have seen the uses of wildlife change over the past 100 years.

Wildlife is no longer essential to sustain life for most British Columbians. The last frontier is gone, or at least going fast, although for some the mentality lingers on.

We have developed more sophisticated means of measuring and counting wildlife and assessing its use and its users. We can manipulate some of the habitat and nourish it. We can even nourish the animals themselves when necessary. But in the long run we cannot replace nature.

This is not to deplore as too little the efforts we now make to preserve and enhance habitat. These are vital and productive efforts. But we must realize that the preservation of most wildlife, especially the larger animals, is a war against so-called progress. It might be an expensive "lunch." For example, it could mean forsaking millions of tons of coal in a mountain that is home to a herd of mountain sheep that has specifically adapted through thousands of years to that habitat. To mine the coal means to lose the sheep.

Well, you may say, there are other sheep herds. How important is diversity of wildlife throughout the province? Do we want a province that is, in effect, a giant zoo? A pen full of elk in the Kootenays, a corral of grizzlies on the coast, a coop of waterfowl in the lower mainland, a cage of sheep north of Prince George. Is that the kind of wildlife diversity we want, and deserve?

We will ultimately get what we deserve because we will deserve what we pay for. Can mankind survive with only rats and cockroaches and sparrows to remind him of his heritage of wildlife? What a shoddy survival that would be!

Aldo Leopold said the land is one organism. Man is part of that organism and he must live in harmony with all the other parts. If we do not live in harmony with them we will live in disharmony and that, in the final test, means we will not live at all. We may survive, but life with only cockroaches and rats as our wildlife heritage is not living.

"You are a King, Tristam...
Mark what you leave."

Wildlife Numbers

Wildlife Branch
Ministry of Environment and Parks

In any discussion of wildlife management, one of the most perplexing problems is arriving at an accurate estimate of animal numbers on which management strategies can be based. The inventory of other components of the ecosystems, such as trees, is difficult enough, given the variability of British Columbia and the expense of working in remote and hazardous terrain. The inventory of our animal populations is complicated by the fact that the animals move around and their preferred habitat will vary with season, weather conditions and food availability. Most of all, accurate assessment of animal numbers is costly, with the result that wildlife managers have relied largely on indirect methods of estimation and in some cases outright guesses.

Wildlife managers use the results of special studies or animal census conducted locally or elsewhere to provide them with a perspective on imal numbers. Techniques include recording evidence of an animal presence by physical sign (e.g., tracks, nests, lodges, dens, rubbings, droppings, food removal, etc.), body counts, sound (e.g., songs or calls) and odour (e.g., musk and other odours). In many cases studies indicate the types of environments suited to supporting different numbers of animals (i.e., habitat) and this information is used to project probable populations of animals over larger areas. Managers try to use two or more approaches to ensure each estimate of animal numbers is reliable. In all cases, the manager tries to ensure his estimates are precise and accurate enough to meet his management objectives. Technology is helping wildlife managers census animals through use of radios to track animals fitted with radio signalling devices, durable markings on animals (i.e., tatoos, tags), recorded animal calls or remote sensing of habitat (i.e., satellite photography). The use of new drugs and traps also facilitates the capture of animals for marking and census as does the use of modern aircraft, boats, snow machines and off-road vehicles.

The following list of estimated numbers for selected wildlife species in British Columbia was prepared by staff of the Wildlife Branch, Ministry of Environment and Parks. The list illustrates the varied abundance and status of the over 600 wild vertebrate species occurring in British Columbia. Figures shown have been derived by a variety of means. Most represent the best estimate of well informed government field biologists using limited animal census information in selected areas. Other estimates are based on knowledge of the distribution of animals and their habitat and related census. In some cases, estimates have been based on the best opinion of university or other scientists and students who have carried out special studies. In all cases the figures shown are approximations of what is believed to occur in nature at this time. It is acknowledged that the accuracy of the estimates varies given the range of information used to arrive at a figure including the knowledge that the abundance of each species may vary considerably, particularly where it occurs in different parts of the province. All estimates are rounded to more truly reflect their accuracy.

Wildlife Population Estimates and Status, 1987

Species	Season	Estimated No.	Status
Endangered			
American White Pelican	breeding	200-250	stable‡
Burrowing Owl	breeding	1 known pair	fluctuating‡
Sea Otter	spring	350-500	increasing‡
Vancouver Island Marmot	spring	200-300	increasing‡
Large Mammals			
Black Bear	fall	120,000	stable*
Caribou	fall	13,000	stable†
Cougar	fall	3,000	increasing*
Deer — Black-tailed	fall	200,000	decreasing†
— Mule	fall	140,000	increasing†
— White-tailed	fall	42,000	increasing†
Elk — Rocky Mountain	fall	35,000	increasing†
— Roosevelt	fall	2,500	stable to increasing†
Grizzly Bear	fall	12,000	stable*
Moose	fall	170,000	stable to increasing†
Mountain Goat	fall	55,000	stable to increasing†
Mountain Sheep			
— Rocky Mountain	fall	2,500	increasing†
— California	fall	3,000	stable†
— Stone	fall	12,000	stable*
— Dall	fall	500	stable*
Wolf	spring	6,000	increasing*

Birds

Bald Eagle	spring	15,000 adults	stable to
		5,000 immatures	decreasing†
Trumpeter Swan	breeding	less than 100	increasing†
	winter	less than 5,000	
Canada Goose	breeding	30,000	increasing*
Peale's Peregrine Falcon	breeding	200	stable†
Spotted Owl	spring	less than 25	decreasing‡
Barrow's Goldeneye	spring	90,000-130,000	stable*
Ruffed Grouse	summer	3-4 million	fluctuating*

Small Mammals

Badger	summer	500-1,000	increasing*
Spotted Skunk	summer	1,500-3,000	increasing*
Mountain Beaver			
(*Aplodontia rufa*)	summer	2,500-5,000	stable*
Deer Mouse	summer	several billion	stable*
Western Harvest Mouse	summer	2,000-3,000	decreasing*
Beaver	fall		
(*Castor canadensis*)	pre-trapping	400,000-600,000	increasing*
Marten	fall	160,000	stable
Muskrat	fall	3,000,000	fluctuating*
Wolverine	fall	5,000	stable*
White-tailed Jack Rabbit	summer	0-?	decreasing‡
Mountain or Nuttall's			
Cottontail	summer	1,000-2,000	decreasing‡
Spotted Bat	summer	30-60	decreasing‡
Pallid Bat	summer	less than 20	decreasing‡
Fringed Bat	summer	1,000-2,000	fluctuating*
Keen's Bat	summer	1,000-2,000	decreasing*
Townsend's Big-eared Bat	summer	2,000	decreasing*

Amphibians

Pacific Giant Salamander	summer	2,000-5,000	decreasing‡
Tiger Salamander	summer	750-1,000	decreasing‡

Reptiles

Painted Turtle	summer	15,000-20,000	decreasing†
Short Horned Lizard	summer	0-?	decreasing*
Sharptailed Snake	summer	2,000-3,000	decreasing‡
Western Rattlesnake	summer	10,000-20,000	decreasing*
Gopher Snake	summer	10,000-20,000	decreasing*

* best estimate, may include limited census

† estimates based on some census of animals and habitat

‡ special studies

SELECTED BIBLIOGRAPHY

Chapter 1

Ball, Georgiana. 1985. "The Monopoly System of Wildlife Management of the Indians and the Hudson's Bay Company in the Early History of British Columbia." *B.C. Studies*, No. 66, Summer 1985, pp. 37-58.

————. 1981. "A History of Wildlife Management Practices in British Columbia to 1918." M.A. thesis, University of Victoria.

British Columbia, *Sessional Papers 1925-1930*. Provincial Game Warden Annual Reports.

Canada, *Sessional Papers 1879-1909*. Department of Marine & Fisheries Annual Reports.

Innis, Harold A. *The Fur Trade in Canada*. (Toronto: University of Toronto Press, 1970).

Mackenzie, Norman. *The Law of Trap and Fang*. (New York: Carlton Press Inc., 1979).

Chapter 3

Anon. Scrap Book for B.C. Wildlife Branch Prov. Archives. GR961.

Ball, Georgiana. 1985. "The Monopoly System of Wildlife Management of the Indians and Hudson's Bay Company in the Early History of British Columbia," *B.C. Studies*, No. 66, Summer 1985.

British Columbia Game Commission. 1946-57. Annual Game Convention reports. 1961 Game Act. R.S. 1948. C. 135 S.1.

British Columbia, Province of, 1905, 1913-1918. Report of the Provincial Game and Forest Warden.

————. 1920. Annual Report of the Game Conservation Board.

————. 1923-28. Annual Report of the Provincial Game Warden.

————. 1929-33. Report of the Game Commissioner.

————. 1934-56. Report of the Game Commissioner.

————. 1957-74. Annual Report of the Dept. of Recreation and Conservation.

————. 1976-84. Annual Report of the Ministry of Environment.

Butler, F. R. 1956. B.C. Game Commission Procedure Manual.

Environment, Ministry of, 1979. Firearm Act R.S. Chap. 134.

————. 1981. Discussion Paper on a New Wildlife Act for B.C.

————. 1982. Wildlife Act No. 55.

Recreation and Conservation, Dept. of, 1966. Wildlife Act No. 55.

————. 1968. Creston Valley Wildlife Management Area Act. Chap. 14.

Chapter 6

Allen, J. A. 1897. Preliminary Description of a New Mountain Sheep. *The British Northwest Territory Bull. Amer. Mus. Nat. Hist.* 9: 111-14.

———. 1903. Mammals Collected in Alaska and Northwestern British Columbia by the Andrew J. Stone Expedition of 1902. *Bull. Amer. Mus. Nat. Hist.* 19: 521-67.

Benson, W. A. 1950. The effect of orchard spraying on pheasants in the Okanagan Valley with observations on bird life in orchard areas. Unpublished M.A. thesis, University of British Columbia, 90pp.

Bergerud, A. T. and Elliott, J. P. 1986. Dynamics of caribou and wolves in northern British Columbia. *Canad. Journ. Zool.* 64: 1515-29.

Clarke, C. H. D. 1936. Fluctuation in numbers of ruffed grouse *Bonasa umbellus* (Lerine), with special reference to Ontario University studies. *Bid. Ser. Bull.* 41: 1-118.

Cowan, Ian McTaggart. 1945. The Ecological Relationships of the Food of the Columbian Black-tailed Deer in the Coast Forest Region of Southern Vancouver Island. *Ecological Monographs* 15: 109-39.

Criddle, N. 1930. Some natural factors governing the fluctuation of grouse in Manitoba. *Canadian Field Naturalist* 44(1): 77-80.

Elton, Charles. 1942. *Mice, Voles and Lemmings.* Oxford University Press, 496 pp.

Errington, Paul L. 1946. Predation and Vertebrate Populations. *Quarterly Review of Biol.* 21: 144-77; 221-45.

Giles, R. H. 1969. *Wildlife Management Technique.* The Wildlife Soc. Washington, D.C., 623 pp.

Hardin, Garrett. The tragedy of the commons. *Science* 162: 1243-47.

Hatler, David F. 1986. *Studies of radio-collared caribou in Spatsizi Wilderness Park area, British Columbia, 1980-84.* Spatsizi Assoc. for Biolog. Res. Smithers, B.C., 202 pp.

Hatter, J. 1950. "The Moose of Central British Columbia." Unpublished Ph.D. thesis, State College of Washington, Pullman, Washington, 356 pp.

Hewitt, C. Gordon. 1921. *The Conservation of Wildlife in Canada.* Charles Scribners & Sons, N.Y., 343 pp.

Hollister, N. 1912. "Mammals of the Alpine Club Expedition to the Mount Robson Region." *Canadian Alpine Journal.* Special Number, pp. 1-46.

Leopold, Aldo. 1942. *Game Management.* Charles Scribners & Sons, New York (2nd ed.), 481 pp.

Munro, J. A. 1923. "A preliminary report on the relation of various ducks and gulls to the propagation of sockeye salmon at Henderson Lake, Vancouver Island, British Columbia." *Canadian Field Naturalist.* 1923, XXXVII, Nos. 5 & 6: 81-83; 107-16.

Nice, Margaret M. 1937-43.

Riley, J. H. 1912. "Birds collected or Observed on the Expedition of the Alpine Club of Canada to Jasper Park, Yellowhead Pass and Mount Robson Region." *Canadian Alpine Journal.* Special Number, pp. 47-75.

Sheldon, Charles. 1911. *The wilderness of the upper Yukon.* Charles Scribners & Sons, New York, 354 pp.

Stoddard, H. L. 1936. "Relations of Burning to Timber and Wildlife" (pp. 399-403) in *Wildlife Restoration and Conservation.* Proc. N. Amer. Wildlife Conference called by President Franklin D. Roosevelt. Washington, D.C., 475 pp.

Tinbergen, N. 1939. "On the analysis of social organization among vertebrates with special reference to birds." *American Midland Nat.* 21: 210-34.

Chapter 11

The Association of British Columbia Professional Foresters. 1983. "A renewable resources position on hydro dams and powerlines." A report to the Government of British Columbia. Vancouver, B.C., 20 pp.

Bird, P. M. and D. J. H. Rappart. 1986. "State of the environment report for Canada." Environment Canada. Ottawa, Ont., 263 pp.

The British Columbia Natural Resources Conference. 1964. "Inventory of the natural resources of British Columbia." Third Inventory, 610 pp.

Bunnell, F. L. and D. S. Eastman. 1976. "Effects of forest management practices on wildlife in the forests of British Columbia," pp. 631-86. In *Proceedings of the 16th Congress of the International Union of Forest Organizations: World Congress, Norway.*

Cail, R. E. 1974. *Land, man, and the law: the disposal of Crown lands in British Columbia, 1871-1913.* The University of British Columbia Press, Vancouver, B.C., 333 pp.

Demarchi, D. A. 1985. "A regional wildlife ecosystem classification for British Columbia." Paper presented to Wildlife Working Group of the Canadian Committee of Ecological Land Classification, Lac Ste. Marie, Quebec, 10 pp.

Farley, A. L. 1976. *Atlas of British Columbia: people, environment and resource use.* The University of British Columbia Press, Vancouver, B.C., 136 pp.

Haig-Brown, R. 1961. *The Living Land: an account of the natural resources of British Columbia.* The Macmillan Company of Canada Ltd., Toronto, Ont., 269 pp.

Pearse, P. H. 1976. *Timber rights and forest policy in British Columbia.* Report of the Royal Commission on Forest Resources. British Columbia, Queen's Printer, Victoria, B.C. Two volumes: 395 and 112 pp.

Ramsay, B. 1968. *Mining in focus: an illustrated history of mining in B.C.* Agency Press, Vancouver, B.C., 149 pp.

Simpson-Lewis, Wendy, Jennifer E. Moore, Nancy J. Popcock, M. C. Taylor and Hedley Swan. 1979. *Canada's special resource lands: a national perspective of selected land uses.* Map Folio No. 4. Environment Canada, Lands Directorate Ottawa, Ont., 232 pp.

The Wilderness Advisory Committee. 1986. "The wilderness mosaic." The Report of the Wilderness Advisory Committee, Vancouver, B.C., 132 pp. plus appendices.

Contributor's Acknowledgements

Everybody owes something to somebody. Here are the acknowledgements that the contributors in this book want to register.

James Hatter

In writing this history of the fur trade in British Columbia, I am appreciative to the British Columbia historian, Georgiana Ball, author of "The Monopoly System of Wildlife Management of the Indians and the Hudson's Bay Company in the Early History of British Columbia." I also have made liberal use of her Master's thesis, "A History of Wildlife Management Practices in British Columbia to 1918." I am particularly grateful to her for her constructive criticism and suggested revisions.

David J. Spalding

Many people have helped me with this chapter. I wish to give special thanks to the following: A. Ackerman, R. Aldrich, A. Breitkrutz, W. Cibulka, L. Cox, C. Estlin, T. Fraser, A. Frisby, J. Gibault, E. Jacobson, R. Jollett, J. Merriman, G. Paull, R. Ritcey, W. Ward, I. Withler.

CONTRIBUTORS

Vernon Cuthbert (Bert) Brink (Natural History Societies). A director and past president of the Federation of B.C. Naturalists representing the Vancouver Natural History Society; professor emeritus — Plant Sciences, U.B.C.; member of many organizations including Ecological Society of America, Sigma Xi, the Agricultural Institute of Canada, and the Alpine Club of Canada.

Ian MacTaggart Cowan (Science and Conservation). Born Edinburgh, 1910. Educated in Vancouver and California (Ph.D., 1935). Professor at U.B.C. 1940-76, retiring as Dean of Graduate Studies. Served many organizations including Wildlife Society (president), Arctic Institute (Chairman), IUCN (Vice-Chairman). Research includes 260 publications on wildlife and conservation. Honours include Order of Canada, Leopold Medal of The Wildlife Society, and Fellow, Royal Society of Canada.

Dennis A. Demarchi (Habitat — The Vital Element) is a professional wildlife biologist with experience in habitat resource mapping and a philosophy of land use in which wildlife needs are considered on equal terms with other resources.

Raymond A. Demarchi (Habitat — The Vital Element) has twenty-two years' experience as a professional regional biologist where he pioneered innovative big game hunting regulations and strongly advocated co-ordinated resource management planning.

Mike Halleran (The Hunting Tradition). A journalist, film maker and broadcaster for most of his working life, he has specialized in natural resources reporting and won many awards for his work. He advises the B.C. Wildlife federation on communications and is the host and producer of the TV series *Westland*, a current affairs program on natural resources, shown on the Knowledge Network of B.C.

Lyn Hancock (The Predator Hunters). Born in Australia, she has taught in Australia, Africa, England and Canada and has written extensively on natural history. She is the author and retains copyright of the book *Cat of Many Names and Faces: The Story of the Controversial Cougar* from which much of the material in her chapter was drawn. She is also the author of *Looking For The Wild: A 30,000 Mile Journey Around North America.*

James Hatter (B.C.'s First Industry — The Fur Trade). Educated at Lake Cowichan, Victoria College, U.B.C., Washington State University (Ph.D.). First game biologist in B.C., commencing career with B.C. Game Commission in 1947. Appointed Director of Fish and Game Branch 1962.

David R. Hurn (Wildlife — Our Talent of Silver) is a professional fisheries biologist with thirty-three years' experience throughout British Columbia in the Fish and Wildlife Branch. His interests range from woodworking to regional planning.

Allan Murray, editor, has a background in education, journalism, and public administration in the fields of natural resources and environmental management in Manitoba and British Columbia.

Donald J. Robinson (Wildlife and the Law) has a graduate degree in wildlife from U.B.C. After nine years as a field biologist and twenty-five years in technical and administrative posts he spent eight years as Director of Fish and Wildlife. He was president of the N.W. Section of The Wildlife Society, and President of the Western Association of Fish and Wildlife Agencies. Now retired, he is a director of the B.C. Wildlife Federation and the Conservation Foundation of B.C.

Leo Rutledge (The Growth of Guiding). Born in the U.S.A. and raised in Norway, he has spent sixty years in the Peace-Liard ranges as a trapper, packer, outfitter and big game guide. Throughout those years he was active in environmental affairs and in the formation of the B.C. Guide Outfitter's Association.

David J. Spalding (The Law and the Poacher) is a professional biologist with experience in marine mammals and wildlife. He was a regional director in the Ministry of Environment and is now a consulting biologist living on South Pender Island.

Lee Straight (Wildlife Societies) was for thirty-three years the full-time outdoor editor of the *Vancouver Sun* and subsequently, for five years, the recreational fisheries advisor-ombudsman with the federal Department of Fisheries and Oceans.